LIFE SCIENCE LIBRARY

MATHEMATICS

OTHER BOOKS BY THE EDITORS OF LIFE

LIFE WORLD LIBRARY

LIFE NATURE LIBRARY

THE LIFE HISTORY OF THE UNITED STATES

LIFE PICTORIAL ATLAS OF THE WORLD

THE EPIC OF MAN

THE WONDERS OF LIFE ON EARTH

THE WORLD WE LIVE IN

THE WORLD'S GREAT RELIGIONS

THE LIFE BOOK OF CHRISTMAS

LIFE'S PICTURE HISTORY OF WESTERN MAN

THE LIFE TREASURY OF AMERICAN FOLKLORE

AMERICA'S ARTS AND SKILLS

THE SECOND WORLD WAR

LIFE'S PICTURE HISTORY OF WORLD WAR II

PICTURE COOK BOOK

LIFE GUIDE TO PARIS

LIFE SCIENCE LIBRARY

CONSULTING EDITORS
René Dubos
Henry Margenau
C. P. Snow

MATHEMATICS

by David Bergamini
and the Editors of LIFE

TIME INCORPORATED, NEW YORK A STONEHENGE BOOK

ABOUT THIS BOOK

A HISTORICAL SURVEY of a science that is an essential tool of all other sciences constitutes the main theme of the text chapters and picture essays in this volume. With a strong emphasis on the people who figured notably in this history, the book traces the ascent of mathematics from simple counting to such recondite studies as topology and transfinite numbers. In addition, it explores some of the ways in which mathematics has contributed precision to the other sciences and extracted new challenges from their findings.

The text chapters are complemented by the picture essays that follow them. In some instances the essays illustrate the subject in depth, sometimes by introducing supplementary materials. Chapters and essays make up a unified whole, but they can also be read independently. For example, Chapter 4 describes the development of analytic geometry; the following essay depicts the link between geometry and esthetics in nature and art.

The much-discussed "new mathematics" now taught in many U.S. schools is explained and evaluated in the Appendix.

THE AUTHOR

DAVID BERGAMINI is a freelance writer specializing in scientific subjects. In writing *Mathematics*, he returns to a subject which first fascinated him as a teenager in a Japanese internment camp in World War II; among the few books available were texts on algebra, geometry and trigonometry. Author of the LIFE Nature Library volume, *The Universe*, he also helped prepare *The World We Live In* as an editor of LIFE. His essay, "The Language of Science," appears in anthologies.

THE CONSULTING EDITORS

RENE DUBOS, a member and professor of The Rockefeller Institute, is a microbiologist and experimental pathologist world-famous for his pioneering in antibiotics, including the discovery of tyrothricin. He has written, among other books, *Mirage of Health* and *The Dreams of Reason*.

HENRY MARGENAU is Eugene Higgins professor of physics and natural philosophy at Yale, an editor of the *American Journal of Science* and a notable contributor to spectroscopy and nuclear physics. His books include *Open Vistas* and *The Nature of Physical Reality*.

C. P. SNOW has won an international audience for his novels, including *The New Men*, *The Search* and *The Affair*, which explore the scientist's role in contemporary society. Trained as a physicist, he directed recruitment of scientific personnel for Britain's Ministry of Labour in World War II. He was knighted in 1957.

ON THE COVER

An airy model of the spiraling helix joins two shapes found in all forms by mathematics: curve and line. The helix makes a familiar functional appearance in the ordinary screw. On the back cover are Babylonian symbols for addition, subtraction, multiplication, division.

CONTENTS

TIME-LIFE BOOKS

EDITOR
Norman P. Ross

TEXT DIRECTOR ART DIRECTOR
William Jay Gold Edward A. Hamilton

CHIEF OF RESEARCH
Beatrice T. Dobie

Assistant Text Director: Jerry Korn
Assistant Chief of Research: Monica O. Horne

PUBLISHER
Rhett Austell

General Manager: John A. Watters
Business Manager: John D. McSweeney
Circulation Manager: Joan D. Lanning

LIFE MAGAZINE

EDITOR: Edward K. Thompson
MANAGING EDITOR: George P. Hunt
PUBLISHER: Jerome S. Hardy

LIFE SCIENCE LIBRARY

Editorial staff for *Mathematics:*

EDITOR: Robert Claiborne
Associate Editor: Robert G. Mason
Text Editor: Diana Hirsh
Picture Editor: John MacDonald
Designer: Arnold C. Holeywell
Staff Writers: Tom Alexander, Stephen Espie,
Alfred Lansing, John Stanton, Paul Trachtman
Chief Researcher: Sheila Osmundsen
Researchers: David Beckwith, Norbert S. Baer,
Doris C. Coffin, Beatrice M. Combs, Mollie Cooper,
Robert H. Cowen, Elizabeth Evans, John L.
Hochmann, Leonard Lipton, Victor Waldrop
Picture Researchers: Margaret K. Goldsmith,
Sue Thalberg Bond
Art Associate: Robert L. Young
Art Assistants: James D. Smith,
Charles Mikolaycak, John M. Woods
Copy Staff: Marian Gordon Goldman,
Suzanne Seixas, Dolores A. Littles

The text for this book was written by David Bergamini, for the picture essays by the staff. The following individuals and departments of Time Inc. were helpful in producing the book: Alfred Eisenstaedt, LIFE staff photographer; Margaret Sargent, LIFE film editor; Doris O'Neil, Chief, LIFE Picture Library, Richard M. Clurman, Chief, TIME-LIFE News Service; and Content Peckham, Chief, Bureau of Editorial Reference.

INTRODUCTION

EARLY man lived in fear and awe of natural events because he could not explain them. Myth and magic dominated his thinking. Then, gradually, he began to understand nature, and learned to enjoy and control her. Historians speak of the epoch in which this understanding began to affect Western culture as the Enlightenment.

Today that phrase has lost some of its meaning. The principles of the Enlightenment, sufficient to let us live in peace with the beasts of the forest, with the tides of the ocean, with thunder and lightning, are inadequate to still our new disquietude about rockets, computers, bevatrons and the superstrains of bacteria engendered by wonder drugs. We live again in a world of magic, this time man-made, and we seek our uncertain way among the robots which, some say, threaten our existence.

A second Enlightenment is now needed in which man can live in peace with his own discoveries and creations, enabled by fuller comprehension to use them for his enrichment and his pleasure. The shift of emphasis from the old-style humanities to science in our school curricula indicates an awareness of this need. Yet it cannot be fulfilled by ordinary educational means. I estimate optimistically that, in my 30 years of college teaching, I may have inculcated what is called the scientific spirit in perhaps 5,000 students. The scientific books available, although large in number, are read by a relatively small group of Americans. Clearly we require books with sufficient appeal and persuasive power to enlighten the intelligent but scientifically uninformed multitudes.

When the Editors of LIFE decided to publish a series of books on science, with the aid of their arsenal of editorial and graphic talent and with a responsible concern befitting scholars, my hopes soared. Here is promising evidence that the new Enlightenment may come to pass, that the cultural gap between our technology and its meaning in terms of human values may be narrowed and finally bridged.

With these high hopes I greet the publication of the present volume, the first of a series on the physical and biological sciences. It is particularly appropriate that it should deal with mathematics, which has a usefulness and a prestige sufficient for it to merit the title "Queen of the Sciences," indispensable to all the rest.

Henry Margenau
*Eugene Higgins Professor of Physics
and Natural Philosophy, Yale University*

1

Numbers:
A Long Way from
One to Zero

MATHEMATICAL BEGINNINGS
An intent first-grader struggles
to learn the ways of numbers. In the process
she is repeating the earliest stages
of man's mathematical development: counting
is as old as prehistoric man; after he had
learned to count, man invented words
for numbers and, later still, symbolic numerals.

SOME DAY, radio astronomers believe, one of their colleagues will experience the enormous excitement of receiving man's first message from intelligent beings on the planet of another star. If they are right—and there is every scientific reason to think that they may be—how will they decode the message? What on earth, or not on earth, could beings different from us in evolutionary background, and probably also in biological structure, say that we could understand? After pondering the problem, scientists have concluded that the one kind of message most likely to make sense to any intelligent form of life anywhere would be a mathematical one.

An advanced extraterrestrial race might broadcast a simply coded bit of arithmetic, for instance, and keep repeating it as a standing call-signal. "Beep, beep-beep, beep-beep-beep" might signify "Counting, one, two, three." "Dot-dash-dot"—pause—"dot-dot" might mean "One plus one equals two." Once simple signals of this sort had been picked up and acknowledged, whole batches of mathematical facts and formulas could be exchanged to establish a basic vocabulary for further communication.

At the National Radio Observatory in Green Bank, West Virginia, radio astronomers have actually pointed giant saucer-shaped antennas at the two stars, Tau Ceti and Epsilon Eridani, to listen for mathematically organized beeps. That this effort has been made in all earnestness underscores a quality of universality in mathematics that everyone feels but no one knows how to define. Many of the world's greatest thinkers, intoxicated by this indefinable something, have decided that mathematics represents absolute truth. "God ever geometrizes," said Plato. "God ever arithmetizes," echoed the 19th Century Prussian Carl Gustav Jacob Jacobi. In our own time the British physicist Sir James Jeans declared, "The Great Architect of the Universe now begins to appear as a pure mathematician."

Today, although mathematicians affirm the universality of their subject, they deny that it possesses any absolute qualities of truth. In fact, one of their favorite definitions of mathematics is Bertrand Russell's witty summation: "the subject in which we never know what we are talking about nor whether what we are saying is true." This definition reflects not modesty but as proud and Promethean a boast as man has ever made. In effect mathematicians are saying that their work can apply to our world and universe because they designed it to apply to every possible world and universe that might be constructed along logical lines. They are saying that mathematics reaches into a realm of such ultimate sophistication that the truth or nontruth of any given premise no longer matters. What does matter, they say, is that the premise be correctly reasoned to its conclusion. Using this criterion, a mathematician could unblinkingly assume that the moon was made of green cheese, and convincingly argue, through a series of further premises, to the conclusion that astronauts should carry crackers.

Mathematics is not so much a body of knowledge as a special kind of language, one so perfect and abstract that—hopefully—it may be understood by intelligent creatures throughout the universe, however different their organs of sense and perception. The grammar of the language—its proper usage—is determined by the rules of logic. Its vocabulary consists of symbols, such as:

numerals for numbers;

letters for unknown numbers;

equations for relationships between numbers;

π for the ratio of the circumference to the diameter of a circle;

sin (for sine), cos (for cosine) and tan (for tangent) for the ratios between sides in a right triangle;

$\sqrt{}$ for a square root;

∞ for infinity;

$\sum$, $\int$, ∂ and $\rightarrow$ for assorted other concepts in higher mathematics.

All of these symbols are tremendously helpful to the scientist because they serve to short-cut his thinking. To many laymen, however, they make mathematics seem less a universal language than a massive linguistic barrier between the so-called "two cultures" of modern society, represented by the scientists and the humanists.

Only part of the vocabulary of mathematics has been preempted by science. The rest of it—and all of the grammar—remains in the sphere of general human thought. Indeed, mathematics has as much to do with philosophy, economics, military strategy, musical composition, artistic perspective and parlor games as it has to do with atomic physics. Because of its virtuosity, anyone well taught in it can love it with the same warmth that a devotee feels for the ballet, fine silver, antiques or any other adornment of civilization.

In view of its esthetic aspect and its total unconcern with practicality, pure mathematics may seem the most pointless pursuit ever devised by dreamers. But the fact is that pure as well as applied mathematicians are being hired today as hardheaded advisers to industrialists, generals and government planners. Our civilization would scarcely exist without the physical laws and intellectual techniques developed as a by-product of mathematical research. No one can balance his checkbook without applying arithmetic invented by the ancient Mesopotamians and Hindus. No one can build a wall without drawing on techniques of geometric measurement developed by Egyptian mathematicians. It was Greek pioneers of geometry who conceived the idea that the earth might have the shape of a sphere. Classical mathematics, when rescued from the oblivion of the Dark Ages, helped ignite the adventurous spirit of the era of Columbus. The men who wrought the Industrial Revolution gained confidence in machines and what they could do from the partly mathematical, partly scientific investigations of Galileo and Newton. Today, atomic research draws heavily on Einstein's Theory of Relativity, which in turn utilized abstruse 19th Century speculations about geometry.

The two pillars of mathematics in antiquity were arithmetic, the science of numbers, and geometry, the science of shapes and spatial relationships. Over the centuries arithmetic was augmented by algebra, which provided a shorthand notation for doing arithmetic when unknown quantities were involved. In the 17th Century, arithmetic and algebra were unified with geometry in "analytic geometry," which provided a technique for mapping numbers as points on a graph, for converting equations into geometric shapes and for converting shapes into equations. The analytical approach of this new geometry, clarifying one branch of mathematics in terms of another, opened the way to most of the disciplines of higher mathematics—disciplines which are encompassed by the single word "analysis."

The first offspring of analysis was calculus, a system for analyzing change and motion in terms of points or numbers strung together in continuous sequences. This enables scientists to solve problems in dynamics—to understand the ripple of a wave, the arc of a shooting star, indeed all the simpler fluctuations of nature. Calculus remains a stand-by for technologists when they design cars and aim rockets.

Gamblers, pollsters and atoms

Many scientists believed, when calculus first came into use, that it would ultimately let them predict the continuing behavior of every moving thing. But at about the same time, through studying gambling games, mathematicians discovered the laws of probability, which reminded them of the leaven of uncertainty that lurks in almost any sequence of events. Today such laws help set the rate a 50-year-old man must pay on a new insurance policy. They enable pollsters to estimate, from any given sampling of voters, the chances of making an accurate election forecast. And they are used in atomic experiments, to evaluate statistically the buckshot patterns which millions of invisible subatomic particles make when they strike a target at the muzzle end of an atom smasher.

By means of vastly complicated equations evolved out of calculus and analytic geometry, mathematicians conceived of geometric shapes beyond our visual ken—shapes of more than the ordinary dimensions of height, width and depth, shapes with any number of dimensions. They also conceived of infinitely dimensioned spaces to put the shapes in. The concept of more-than-three-dimensional spaces was basic to Einstein's ideas about relativity and the universe. It has also led to solutions for

FOUR FAMILIAR SYMBOLS WRITTEN IN ANTIQUE STYLE

Since early Babylonia mathematicians have saved time and effort by substituting symbols for words. Among such shorthand devices are our numerals and the simple $+$, $-$, $\times$, $\div$ signs which we employ to show the basic arithmetical steps of adding, subtracting, multiplying and dividing. These four key symbols, while automatic in our computations by now, are relatively new in mathematical history. Some early ways of writing them are shown below.

ADDITION
The Renaissance calculator Tartaglia used the first letter of the Italian *più* (plus) to signify adding. Our $+$ sign is probably a shorthand form of the Latin *et* (and).

SUBTRACTION
This minus sign was favored in Greek times by Diophantus. Our subtraction symbol may derive from a bar medieval traders used to mark differences in product weights.

MULTIPLICATION
Our $\times$ sign, based on St. Andrew's Cross, was known when the symbol above was employed by Leibniz in 17th Century Germany. But he found $\times$ too similar to algebra's "unknown" x.

DIVISION
In 18th Century France J.E. Gallimard used this reverse D for division. The sign we use may come from the simple fractional line, embellished by upper and lower dot.

difficult problems about electrical and magnetic fields in the complicated gadgetry of computers and television sets. At the present time practitioners of geometry are pursuing a still further abstraction of their art through "topology," the art of analyzing those properties of a shape which remain unaffected after the shape itself has been shrunk, stretched or twisted.

The logic of all blue eyes

Other mathematicians have reached back to find inspiration in the most elementary mathematical ideas of all. The "number theorists" have returned to the deceptively simple steps we count by, and repeatedly they have found that the integers, or ordinary whole numbers—one, two, three and on up—are the most baffling, stimulating and entertaining of all mathematical subjects. Even the underlying processes of thought itself have become a target for mathematical probes. The meanings of the nouns and the verbs used in ordinary human reasoning, mathematicians say, are subject to different interpretations; why not replace them with symbols as unambiguous as numerals and with operations as unambiguous as addition and multiplication? Proponents of this "symbolic logic" have brooded on ways of reducing all objects of human study to "sets" and "groups"—collections of thoughts or things that go together logically, such as "all blue eyes" or "all women drivers." And they have tried to find strictly logical ways of making non-odious comparisons by matching elements in one set or group with those in another.

The varieties of mathematics sketched above constitute its main mountain ranges. Innumerable spurs and foothills fringe these ranges. Geometry's many branches include projective, affine, Euclidean and Riemannian; algebra's include Banach, Boolean and homological. All these ingenious creations of thought not only have application in everyday life but in a fundamental way also spring from life. When an Amazon Indian blows a poisoned dart at a monkey in a treetop, he intuitively judges a missile trajectory that could be more exactly judged by analysis and the laws of motion. When you step on the gas to pass a car, you risk your life on an estimate that can be made precise through calculus.

Today there is hardly any human activity or thought process—from hunting enemy submarines to composing music—which mathematicians have not sought to reduce to its essential elements. As a result mathematics has kept growing. Its great works are repeatedly rewritten and put in more symmetrical, general, precise and useful terms. This unending revision has helped to keep mathematics—even after some 6,000 years of development—from becoming impossibly bulky and sprawling. Until about a century ago, a gifted mathematician could still hope to master all of it in some detail. Even now a student can get a fairly repre-

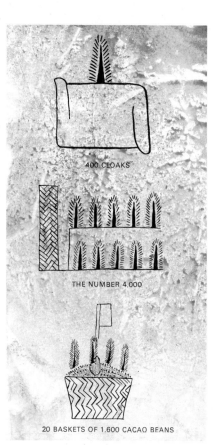

400 CLOAKS

THE NUMBER 4,000

20 BASKETS OF 1,600 CACAO BEANS

PRE-COLUMBIAN NUMBER SYMBOLS
The Aztecs of 15th Century Mexico depicted everyday objects by pictures which often included number symbols. One common symbol, a fringed spike, stood for the number 400. A spike over a picture of a cloak (top) meant "400 cloaks." Ten spikes (middle) signified the number 4,000. Spikes on the basket of cacao beans (bottom) indicated 1,600 beans; the flag on the spikes symbolized 20 baskets.

sentative bird's-eye picture of the whole in order to choose a specialty.

Inevitably the language of mathematics has become far more subtle and difficult than any spoken tongue. Children have a far better chance than adults to become at home in it because they can pick up its symbolic vocabulary and its grammar before they begin worrying unduly about reasons and relationships. The "new mathematics" being taught in many schools today is an attempt to exploit this facility. Many a parent may look askance at his fifth-grader who is at ease with some of the terminology and ideas of symbolic logic, but the fact is that basically the new concepts in advanced mathematics are often far less difficult than the ideas at the bottom of elementary arithmetic. A group of French mathematicians who work under the collective pseudonym of "Monsieur Nicholas Bourbaki" demonstrated this point some years ago when they embarked on an encyclopedic description of all mathematics and found that they had devoted 200 pages simply to introducing the difficulties involved in that innocent-looking concept, the number "one."

While both teaching techniques and problem-solving in mathematics can often be simplified, the abstract fundamentals can never be made easy. About 2,300 years ago, it is said, Alexander the Great asked a Greek mathematician, Menaechmus, for a quick explanation of geometry. The answer was tart: "There is no royal road to geometry." Menaechmus' answer still holds good, and for all branches of mathematics. The professionals who have traveled the road naturally feel a mixture of superiority and helplessness toward all the inquiring modern Alexanders who would like to make a jet-paced conquest of the whole terrain.

Fortunately, just as it is not necessary to become fluent in the language of a country in order to appreciate the character of its people, so it is not necessary to be able to say

$$\lim_{\Delta x_i \to 0} \sum_{i=1}^{m} f(x_i) \Delta x_i$$

to a mathematician—or even to pronounce it properly—in order to appreciate the main branches of his subject, to know what they are about, why they are exciting and valuable, and how they have come into being.

Mathematics began with the invention of numbers to count by. Prehistoric man's need to count at all was limited, if we can judge by his latter-day kin, the surviving Stone Age tribesmen of Australia, New Guinea and Brazil. Many do not have names for numbers beyond 2 or 3. No doubt part of the reason is that they live in small family groups and are poor in possessions. Probably, too, they have few words to represent whole groups of things which might be counted. Some of them, for instance, are instinctive botanists who can recognize and name hundreds of separate species of trees but have no general word for "tree" itself. A Brazilian Indian chief is likely to react with scorn to the

PRE-COLUMBIAN CALCULATOR
Accounts in the Inca Empire of Peru (12th to 16th Centuries) were kept by a so-called "grand treasurer." Using an abacus with maize kernels *(bottom),* he then transposed his computations to a quipu, or series of wool cords attached to a long rope. Knots tied in the cords provided a permanent record of taxes, expenses and vital statistics.

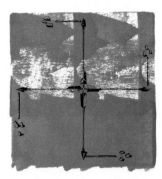

A PRIMITIVE WAY OF COUNTING
This crude swastika laid out on the ground
is the number 21 as "written" by the Pueblo
Indians of our Southwest. Each of the
four arrows in the swastika stands for 1.
The "mystical middle," where the arrows meet
is worth 1. Each stick at the end of an arrow
and each pebble at the end of a stick are
also worth 1. Four arrows, 1 mystical middle,
4 sticks and 12 pebbles equal 21. Other numbers
were constructed by using pebbles, arrows
and sticks in a variety of other combinations.

question "How many?" If pressed, he can usually summon a special
medicine man—anthropologists actually call the man a "numerator"—to
invent compound-number names out of 1s, 2s and 3s, and to recite them
ceremoniously after each possession the chief may list.

When the glaciers retreated about 10,000 years ago, some nomadic
Stone Age hunters in the hill country of the Middle East evolved a new
way of life: farming. At once they faced the problems of keeping track of
days and seasons, and of knowing what quantities of food grain and seed
grain to store. As more complex agricultural societies developed in the
valleys of the Nile, Tigris and Euphrates, the farmer confronted a further problem: paying taxes. All these prerequisites of civilization required that numbers be given names and that counting be elaborated
beyond the primitive notions of "one" and "many."

Fingers, toes and old scores

Some ancient tribes, it is believed, used a base of 2 to count by: 1, 2,
2-1, 2-2, 2-2-1 and so on. Others used a base of 3: 1, 2, 3, 3-1, 3-2, 3-3,
3-3-1 and so on. As they became farmers and builders, the most advanced peoples pushed their basic counting limit higher. Many used
their own fingers and toes as the handiest counters, thus amassing new
numbers all the way up to 20—at which point fingers and toes ran out.
Early 20-based number systems are still remembered in the French
words for 80 and 90, "quatre-vingt" and "quatre-vingt-dix," which mean
"four-twenty" and "four-twenty-ten," and in the British 20-shilling pound.

(The British monetary system itself, with its ha'pennies, pennies,
threepence, sixpence, shillings, half crowns, pounds and guineas, is a
$\frac{1}{2}$-1-3-6-12-30-240-252 system—a mixture of several archaic systems that
has been perpetuated to confound foreigners.)

Whatever the system they used for counting, the merchants of the
early civilizations presumably used pebbles piled up on the ground to
represent the numbers counted. It was probably out of such a method
that we acquired the computing device known as the abacus, which is
still standard equipment in bazaars from Tehran to Hong Kong. The
abacus may have begun as a sort of poker pot in which a certain kind
of chip would stand for 1, another for 10, another for 100. Eventually,
varieties of the abacus were evolved. Some were mechanically organized
so that the one-chips slid on one bar, the ten-chips on another, the hundred and ten-hundred chips on a third and fourth. By flipping these
counters up and down, the ancient traders could add and subtract faster
than most people can with pencil and paper today.

The skillful use of tally-tokens for handling financial calculations may
have retarded the perfection of written numbers. And it was from the
development of written notations for numbers that modern arithmetic

AN INSTINCTIVE EYE FOR GEOMETRY
Primitive art clearly shows that people with
little mathematical training may even so
have an inborn feel for geometric shapes. The
Egyptian, Cypriot and Etruscan pottery all
date from before Christ. Contemporary masks
and fabrics made by tribes in Peru and Africa
have precise pattern and boldness of line.

EGYPTIAN BOWL   CONGOLESE MASK

and modern algebraic ideas were to grow. One of the crudest ways of writing numbers is preserved for us in the Roman numerals I, II, III, IV, V, VI and so on. Essentially this is a technique in which every number is expressed as the addition or subtraction of a few basic symbols. We use a similar system when we keep a score by /, //, ///, ////, ////.

It is believed that the written symbols for numbers which we use today—1, 2, 3, 4, 5, 6, 7, 8 and 9—originated with the Hindus. They were devised to go with a 10-based, or "decimal," method of counting, so named after the Latin word *decima*, meaning tenth, or tithe. The way we put our numbers together seems simple enough, but it is in fact the artful product of centuries of development—what the mathematicians call a "positional notation." In this system the position of each digit in a sequence of numerals decides its value. The numbers larger than 1 are separated from the numbers smaller than 1 (the fractions) by a decimal point. To the left of the point, the first digit is worth just itself; the next digit is worth itself times 10; the next digit, itself times 100; the next digit, itself times 1,000, and so on. To the right of the decimal point, the first digit is worth $1/10$ of itself; the next digit, $1/100$ of itself; the next digit, $1/1,000$ of itself, and so on.

The number 8,765.4321, for example, means $8 \times 1,000 + 7 \times 100 + 6 \times 10 + 5 \times 1 + 4 \times 1/10 + 3 \times 1/100 + 2 \times 1/1,000 + 1 \times 1/10,000$. Ultimately a shorthand device was invented, the so-called "power," or "exponent," by which the number 8,765.4321 can also be expressed as $8 \times 10^3 + 7 \times 10^2 + 6 \times 10^1 + 5 \times 10^0 + 4 \times 10^{-1} + 3 \times 10^{-2} + 2 \times 10^{-3} + 1 \times 10^{-4}$. In the case of 10^3, the number 3 indicates the "power," and is another way of signifying $10 \times 10 \times 10$, or 1,000. Similarly, the negative exponents are used to denote the decimal fractions. Thus, 10^{-3} means $1/10^3$ or $1/1,000$ or .001.

Within this system of powers, a question sometimes arises as to the meaning of 10^0, or 10 to the zero power. From our 8,765.4321 sequence, it will be apparent that 10^0 lies between 10^1 and 10^{-1}, or between 10 and $1/10$, and it is defined as equal to 1. This neat symmetry of powers extends to other numbers besides 10, and except for zero itself, every number raised to the zero power is defined as equal to 1.

In the counting system we use today—the decimal positional notation system, to give it its full title—we use a base of 10. But there is absolutely no reason—except perhaps the number of fingers on a pair of human hands—that we do not instead write numbers with a base of 12 or 20. For over half the course of civilization the scientists of the Western world wrote their fractions by a positional notation system on a different base. This was a breathtakingly sophisticated "sexagesimal" system worked out by the ancient Mesopotamians on the number 60.

Although 60 is an extraordinarily large number to use as the base for

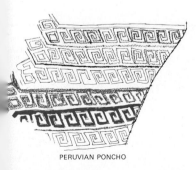

PERUVIAN PONCHO

CYPRIOT JUG

CONGOLESE WEAVING

ETRUSCAN VASE

CONGOLESE WEAVING

a notation system, we still use it every day in our division of an hour into 60 minutes, of a minute into 60 seconds, and of a circle into six times 60°. If a naval officer tells his men to synchronize their watches at 5:07:09, they know that he means nine seconds and seven minutes after 5 a.m. Few would be able to decipher the ancient 60-based number 5,7,9 (by which the Mesopotamians meant $5 \times 60^2 + 7 \times 60^1 + 9 \times 60^0$), but if they could they would arrive at the modern number 18,429. And that is what 5:07:09 means: exactly 18,429 seconds after midnight.

The 60-system had one important drawback born of its broad base. To represent each number from zero to 59, the Mesopotamians faced the prospect of devising 59 separate symbols. No one, not even the number-loving Sumerians and Babylonians who successively inhabited Mesopotamia, ever wanted to memorize 59 numerals any more than we today relish memorizing over 120 telephone area codes. To get around this difficulty, the ancients used combinations of two wedge-shaped symbols, one representing the number 1, the other representing the number 10.

The many-splendored 60

With its one disadvantage, the 60-system also had certain virtues. The number 60 can be evenly divided by 1, 2, 3, 4, 5, 6, 10, 12, 15, 20, 30 and 60, whereas 10 can be evenly divided only by 1, 2, 5 and 10. This means that arithmetic problems worked out in the 60-system more frequently came out in even answers than they do in the 10-system. What was perhaps more important to the Mesopotamians, who were avid astronomers, the base of 60 fitted well with their division of a year into 360 days.

The 60-system came into being before 1700 B.C. Cuneiform tablets of this era show that by then it was already being used for amazing feats of computation by mathematicians of the reign of Babylon's intellectual King Hammurabi. But as yet they had no symbol for zero. To indicate an empty position in a number sequence, they left a gap. But since they often forgot to do so, the numbers were sometimes ambiguous.

By about 300 B.C., the era of the next great group of cuneiform tablets which archeologists have unearthed, a symbol for zero had appeared —a mark somewhat resembling an upended W. During this period the Persians ruled Mesopotamia, and the 60-system showed a considerable development beyond its original form. Mathematicians were carrying out their calculations to seventeen 60-system places, or what in our present notation would amount to 29-digit numbers. The prodigious nature of this achievement can be gauged by a look at a 60-system sequence of a mere four places. If, for instance, the Persians wished to express the number five million eleven thousand one hundred and sixty-seven, they did it as 23,11,59,27—which means $23 \times 60^3 + 11 \times 60^2 + 59 \times 60^1 + 27 \times 60^0$ (4,968,000 + 39,600 + 3,540 + 27 = 5,011,167).

SIX WAYS TO WRITE 1 TO 10
Most of these old notations *(right)* show the influence of early notch-cutting by primitive man. The first four notations further developed according to the writing tools and surfaces used: Babylonian, stylus on clay; Egyptian hieratic, pen on papyrus; Mayan, sticks and pebbles; Chinese, pen on paper. Greek numerals were formed from the letters of their alphabet. Roman numerals, it is believed, evolved from finger-counting.

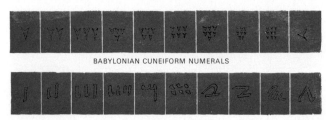

BABYLONIAN CUNEIFORM NUMERALS

EGYPTIAN HIERATIC NUMERALS

The 60-system outlasted the Mesopotamians who fathered it because its positional notation remained, for centuries, the only one extant. Greek astronomers and their Hindu counterparts in the early Christian era used it to record, in positional form, the fractions involved in charting the heavens. The Greeks and Hindus also utilized the 10-system, but only for simple counting, since at that stripling stage of its development the 10-system lacked a positional notation. The letters of the Greek and Hindu alphabets served as symbols for the decimal numbers.

Then, probably around 500 A.D., some Hindu devised a positional notation for the decimal system. The Hindus threw out the now-needless letter symbols they had used for numbers higher than 9 and standardized the symbols for the first nine. Although subsequently modernized, these nine Hindu letter symbols are what we today know as numbers 1 through 9. The all-important zero sign did not come along until the decimal positional notation had been further developed.

The first great popularizer of this notation was an Arab mathematician, al-Khowarizmi of Baghdad, who around 825 wrote a book on the Indian numerals in which he commended the new technique from the East to mathematicians and merchants everywhere. They were slow to heed his sage advice. It took the new numbers about two centuries to reach Spain, where they were reconstituted in a recognizably modern script known as the Ghobar numerals—so called, it is thought, after the Arabic word for dust, or sand, which occasionally was used in a sort of computational sandbox. By the late 13th Century the city-state of Florence was passing laws against the use of the upstart decimal numerals to protect honest citizens from the easy changes which forgers of bank drafts, for instance, could ring on the numbers 0, 6 and 9. At about the same time the new number-writing technique arrived in England in a book called *Crafte of Nombrynge*.

The triumph of the decimal

The 10-based positional notation system ultimately won out over earlier systems because it was taken up by European merchants. Most likely the Araby-Indy experts in the counting houses of the larger shipping firms of Genoa and Hamburg found that they could do accounts faster than colleagues who specialized, say, in Roman numerals. The enthusiasm of the businessmen was not initially shared by the scientists and scholars, and for good reason. As yet the decimal system had no easy way to denote fractions. For this vital aspect of computation, learned circles continued to rely upon the ancient 60-system.

For our own convenient way of designating decimal fractions—$.23 for 23/100 of a dollar, or .365 for a ballplayer's batting average—we can thank certain inventive thinkers of both Asia and Europe. One

HINDU (BRAHMI), C. 300 B.C.

HINDU (GWALIOR), 876 A.D.

HINDU (DEVANAGARI), 11TH CENTURY

WEST ARABIC (GHOBAR), 11TH CENTURY

EAST ARABIC, 1575

EUROPEAN, MOST OF 15TH CENTURY

EUROPEAN, 16TH CENTURY

BANK CHECK NUMERALS, 20TH CENTURY

HOW OUR NUMBERS EVOLVED
Today's familiar numerals derive from early Hindu script and Arabic numerals of Moorish Spain, with subsequent European refinements. The round dot at the end of some rows represents the symbol for zero, whose importance the Arabs recognized in one of the most trenchant sentences in mathematical history: "When [in subtraction] nothing is left over, then write the little circle so that the place does not remain empty."

MAYAN NUMERALS

GREEK ALPHABET NUMERALS

MODERN CHINESE NUMERALS

ROMAN NUMERALS

was al-Kashi, 15th Century director of the astronomical observatory at Samarkand founded by Ulugh Beg, grandson of Tamerlane the Conqueror. Al-Kashi was among the first-known mathematicians to perceive that negative powers could be exploited in the 10-system as well as in the 60-system. A 16th Century German, Christoff Rudolff, produced a further clarifying explanation. Then a Belgian, Simon Stevin, presented the first systematic treatment of the new decimal fractions in a landmark opus entitled *La Disme (The Art of Tenths)*. The decimal point as we know it made its debut in 1617 in a book by a Scotsman, John Napier.

Even today, with all our knowledge, it would be rash to think that we have settled on our final counting system. Not that some relict tribesmen are likely to sweep out of the rain forests and take over the earth, but there are other unconverted heathen of a less flesh-and-blood variety: the robots, or calculating machines. These creatures of man's genius operate by electric switches which can either be "on" or "off." As a result they can count only two numbers: 1 for "on" and 0 for "off." Thus, more and more, modern man is relying on a 2-based, or "binary," system of arithmetic.

Ironically, by the time we hear the first "Beep, beep-beep, beep-beep-beep" from a distant planet, we may have gone back to the counting simplicity of an aborigine, but we will have brought to it, we may hope, the enlightened understanding of an Einstein.

Computing: From Human Fingers to Man-made Brains

Counting is an intricate process; of all the earth's creatures only man can do it. Early humans probably formed numbers with their fingers, as some primitive peoples still do *(opposite)*. As society became more complicated, man had to make fairly elaborate calculations involving subtraction, multiplication and division, and the devices he used to assist him grew more advanced. By the time of the ancient Greeks, mechanical calculators were in use—and in the 2,000 years since then an array of increasingly sophisticated computing machines has been developed. The culmination was the electronic computer, that wonderful "brain" that can do difficult mathematical problems in a split second and is slowly changing our very civilization. There may indeed be some kernel of truth in the exuberant claim of the great mathematician-philosopher Auguste Comte: "There is no inquiry which is not finally reducible to a question of numbers."

PRIMITIVE COMPUTING
Using fingers and other parts of the body, a Sibiller tribesman of New Guinea *(opposite)* can count to 27—no further. He uses the fingers of his right hand to point to those of his left hand (1-5). His left wrist, forearm, elbow, biceps, collarbone, shoulder, ear and eye make up 6 to 13. The nose is 14. He then goes down the right side from eye to little finger for 15 to 27.

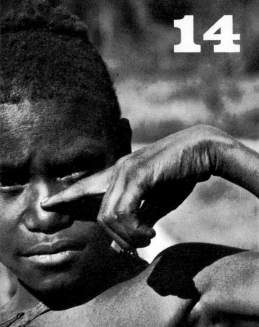

THE ABACUS IN THE ORIENT
A Japanese *(above)* calculates on the beads. The abacus is still the commonest computer in Asia. Some abacus operators there can compute faster than clerks with modern adding machines.

THE ABACUS IN OLD EUROPE
Through most of Europe's history, the abacus was the computer triumphant. An old print *(left)* imagines Boethius and Pythagoras computing, respectively, with written numerals and abacus.

THE ABACUS IN SCHOOL
The Abacounter *(below)*, an adaptation of the abacus, is used by second-graders in Columbus, Ohio. The 12 horizontal bars are for units, and the three vertical bars are for decimal multiples.

COUNTING ON THE BEADS

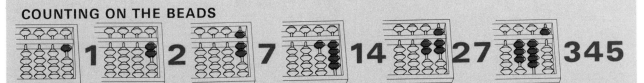

The colored beads of each abacus form the total at its right. Below the crossbar, beads are worth *(right to left):* 1, 10, 100, 1,000; above the bar, 5, 50, 500, 5,000. To register a number, beads must be pushed to the crossbar.

ADDING BY THE ABACUS

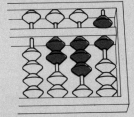 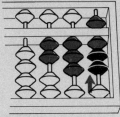 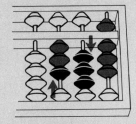 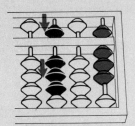

The problem: add 272 to 236. In the first sketch *(left)* the colored beads at the crossbar register 236. The

272 would consist of two 1s, seven 10s, two 100s. The two 1s can be registered (second sketch) but

the seven 10s cannot; instead one 100-bead is added and three 10s subtracted (third sketch), which gives

the equivalent. To add the last 200 (fourth sketch), add one 500-bead, take away three 100s. Result: 508.

A Computer That Has Withstood the Test of Time

The abacus *(above)* is one of those rare inventions that are so simple yet so effective that they are passed on unchanged from civilization to civilization. It may have been 5,000 years ago in ancient Babylonia that man first discovered that if he marked figures on a dust-covered board he could compute faster than with fingers. This "dust board" evolved into the "counter abacus," in which grooves were cut in a board and small disks representing the numerals were moved along the grooves. The Chinese are probably responsible for the refinement we know today, movable beads on rods, and Oriental operators can subtract, multiply and divide as well as add.

Part of an ancient computer.

Mechanical Marvels to Speed the Work of Calculating

In 1900, Greek sponge fishermen found the corroded mechanism above which had been lying on the bottom of the Aegean Sea for 2,000 years. Most historians, who had assumed that the Greeks' technology lagged behind their other achievements, were startled to find that this mechanism came from a complex, geared computer much like a modern mechanical clock.

Mankind's museum of calculators is full of such odd devices. Ranging from vest-pocket size like "Napier's bones" *(below)* to the size of a room like the differential analyzer opposite, they reflect the continuing need of scientists, businessmen and the general public for better and better machines to help them in their counting.

"NAPIER'S BONES"

John Napier's cheap, simple device for multiplying, known as "Napier's bones," was popular in 17th Century Europe. Each of its rods *(above)* contained the digits 1 to 9, with their multiples in columns underneath them. Multiplication was done by rotating the rods in such a way that the answer could be found by adding numbers in horizontally adjacent squares.

PASCAL'S ADDING MACHINE

In 1642 the French philosopher Blaise Pascal, 19 years old and tired of totting up figures for his tax-collector father, invented the fancy machine at left for adding and subtracting. Its cylinders and gears *(foreground)* were housed in a small box *(rear)*. The wheels on the top of this box corresponded to units, 10s, 100s and so on; each wheel could register the digits 0 to 9.

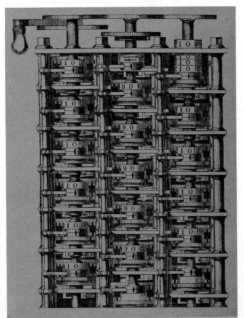

A MAN AHEAD OF HIS TIME

Charles Babbage *(above)*, a 19th Century English inventor, designed his Difference Engine to calculate and print mathematical tables. It failed because parts could not be machined precisely.

BABBAGE'S MULTIPLIER

The computing element (part of it shown at left) of Babbage's elaborate machine for multiplying was a series of toothed wheels on shafts. They worked like the wheels of a modern mileage indicator.

THE END OF AN AGE

The differential analyzer, shown here with its inventor, Dr. Vannevar Bush, is a giant modern mechanical computer built in 1930 at M.I.T. to solve differential equations. A later model, a transition to the electronics age, replaced many of the gears and shafts above with electrical switches. Bush's machine was used to calculate artillery trajectories during World War II.

The Wonderful
Yes-or-No Language
of Punched Cards

The punched card, emblem of the age of electronic computers, was invented nearly 250 years ago, when it was used in a loom *(left)* to speed the weaving of patterned fabrics. But the holed cards really came into their own in 1890 when they were used in a mechanical computer to handle U.S. census figures—at a saving of five million dollars.

Today the punched card is an indispensable tool of the electronic computer. Data are recorded on the cards by punching holes in specific locations. These holes can be "read" by computers in much the same way the loom follows its weaving pattern: the computer's electric current, like the loom's needle, either pierces the card at a given spot or does not, depending on whether there is a hole there.

Since the computer is limited to this pierce or no-pierce response, all numbers being fed into it must be punched into the cards in a code made up of holes or no-holes. All sorts of punched-card codes have been devised, including the basic binary code which operates on the binary number system explained on the opposite page. Binary numbers, made up of combinations of 1 and 0, are represented on the cards by holes and blanks.

WEAVING BY THE CARD
In 1728 a French engineer invented this automatic loom. An endless chain of punched cards was set to rotate past the needles of the loom. As the cards moved by, only the needles which matched holes were able to penetrate, and their threads determined the pattern.

PUNCHING BY MACHINE
By 1890 Herman Hollerith, an American engineer, had perfected the first data-processing machine to use punched cards. The holes had to be punched one by one, but by 1916 the device at right had been patented to solve this problem, punching nine holes in a card at once.

THE DECIMAL SYSTEM OF COUNTING

The familiar decimal system of counting needs just 10 symbols—0 and the digits 1 through 9—to write any number, no matter how large. All the numbers in this convenient system are built up out of blocks valued at 1, 10 and powers of 10 (such as 100, which is 10 x 10; 1,000, which is 10 x 10 x 10; etc.). As is shown in the table under the row of blocks below, to build the number 3 requires three 1-blocks. To build the number 13, for the sign in the grocer's window at right, requires one block of 10 and three blocks of 1. Similarly, 49 needs four 10s and nine 1s; 125 needs one 100-block, two 10s and five 1s. Reading from left to right, every decimal number is a summary of the kinds of blocks it takes to build it up.

COUNTING BY POWERS OF 10

100	10	1	
		3	3
	1	3	13
	4	9	49
1	2	5	125

COUNTING BY POWERS OF 2

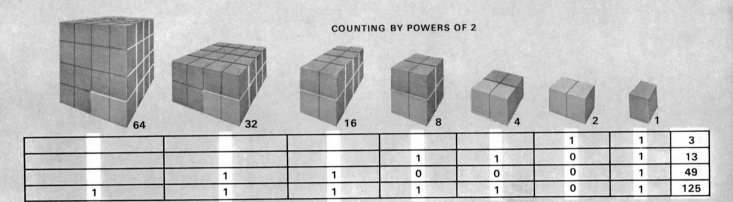

64	32	16	8	4	2	1	
					1	1	3
			1	1	0	1	13
	1	1	0	0	0	1	49
1	1	1	1	1	0	1	125

THE BINARY SYSTEM OF COUNTING

The binary system uses blocks worth 1, 2 and powers of 2 (such as 4, which is 2 x 2; 8, which is 2 x 2 x 2; etc.). To build the number 3 from binary blocks requires one 1-block and one 2-block, so it is written 11. To build binary 13 for the grocery at the right requires one 8-block, one 4-block, no 2-blocks and one 1-block—written as 1101. The number 49 needs one 32, one 16, no 8, no 4, no 2 and one 1—written as 110001. In the same way, 125 is written as 1111101. In the yes-no language of electronic computers, when the binary system writes 100 as 1100100, it is really saying: "A block of 64, yes; a block of 32, yes; a block of 16, no; a block of 8, no; a block of 4, yes; a block of 2, no; a unit, no."

A $10-million computer, Weather Bureau's STRETCH (so called because its developers hoped it would stretch man's knowledge) analyzes

Machines That Can Add in a Millionth of a Second

In 1946 the first electronic computer, the ENIAC at the University of Pennsylvania, did an addition in 1/5000 of a second. The largest U.S. computer today, the Weather Bureau's STRETCH *(above)* with vastly improved circuitry, is able to do the same addition in 1.5 millionths of a second. The secret of such speeds is electricity, which—in contrast to the slower movement of gears and levers in mechanical computers—moves through the transistors of modern electronic computers with nearly the speed of light. In electronic digital computers like ENIAC and STRETCH,

numbers are converted into electrical codes. The code usually used is the binary system *(previous page)*, whose notation of 1s and 0s can be simulated by the switching on and off of electric flow.

Because of their superhuman speeds, computers are often suspected of having superhuman powers. The truth is they do nothing a man could not do—if he had the time. In fact even the simplest problem fed into a computer requires long and thoughtful human processing before it can be solved by the computer's own "thought processes," described on the following pages.

90,000 weather reports at once in a study of long-range forecasting. The colored lights on the components are keyed to the sketch below.

A COMPUTER'S COMPONENTS

In this sketch at right of the IBM STRETCH computer above, the input is colored blue; so is the output, or high-speed printer. The card reader is green. The main memory unit is orange and the main processing unit is violet. STRETCH has a second memory system linked with a second processing system. This unit is in yellow. The control section of a smaller auxiliary computer connected to STRETCH is blue-green.

The Four Steps in Computer "Thinking"

INPUT 1

Like the human brain, the computer must be given the problem and the information it needs to solve it. Feeding such data to the machine is called "input."

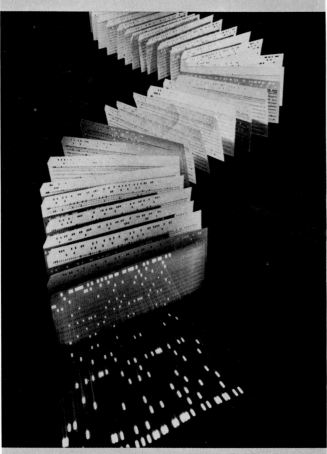

Punch cards are one of the commonest means of feeding information into the computer. A single card may hold, in coded form, as many as 106 digits.

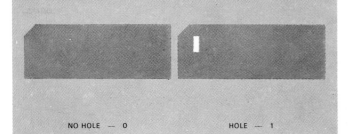

NO HOLE — 0   HOLE — 1

A card using binary code *(pages 24-25)* registers 1 if current pierces a hole, 0 when there is no hole.

MEMORY 2

All of the information a computer needs to solve a problem—and just how it is to use that information—is stored in the computer's memory units *(below)*.

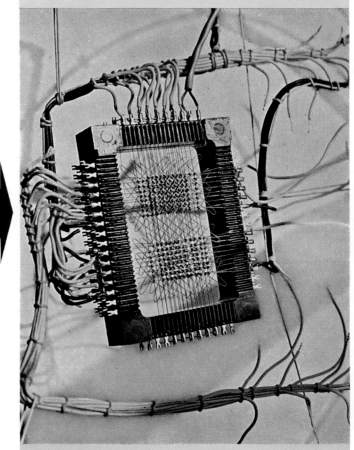

One type of memory is made of many units, like the one above in which wires form a grid with tiny, circular core magnets strung at each intersection.

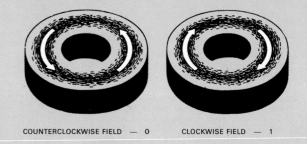

COUNTERCLOCKWISE FIELD — 0   CLOCKWISE FIELD — 1

Data coded as either 1 or 0 are stored by sending current through core magnets in different directions.

PROCESSING 3

In processing, the computer solves its problem. Unlike a human brain, it acts only by rote, using logic provided by a human programmer *(next pages).*

OUTPUT 4

The voice of the computer, its output, produces answers in many forms: punched cards, punched tape, magnetic tape, typewritten sheets of paper *(below).*

The first computers used vacuum tubes in their processing units. Many modern computers use faster and smaller transistorized circuits like those above.

This high-speed output printer on IBM's STRETCH, activated by electronic messages from the computer, types 2,000 characters a second, 600 lines a minute.

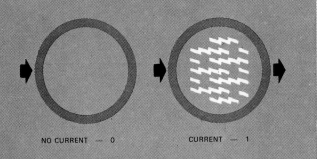

NO CURRENT — 0   CURRENT — 1

A transistor handles the binary notation speedily. No current flowing means 0; current flowing means 1.

A section of the output sheet from STRETCH shows a code used in developing world weather forecasts.

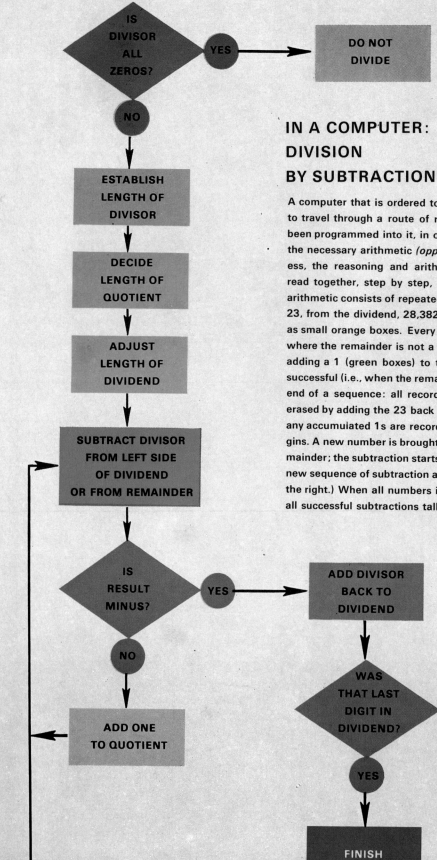

IN A COMPUTER: DIVISION BY SUBTRACTION

A computer that is ordered to divide 28,382 by 23 has to travel through a route of reasoning *(left),* which has been programmed into it, in order to be able to perform the necessary arithmetic *(opposite).* To follow the process, the reasoning and arithmetic columns should be read together, step by step, matching the colors. The arithmetic consists of repeatedly subtracting the divisor, 23, from the dividend, 28,382. These subtractions are shown at the right as small orange boxes. Every time a successful subtraction is made (i.e., where the remainder is not a minus number), the machine chalks it up by adding a 1 (green boxes) to the quotient. Whenever a subtraction is unsuccessful (i.e., when the remainder comes out a minus number), that is the end of a sequence: all record of the unsuccessful subtraction attempt is erased by adding the 23 back to the minus remainder (pale orange boxes), any accumulated 1s are recorded in the quotient, and a new sequence begins. A new number is brought down from the dividend and added to the remainder; the subtraction starts again. (Notice that any 1s resulting from this new sequence of subtraction are added to the quotient one place farther to the right.) When all numbers in the dividend have been brought down and all successful subtractions tallied in the quotient, the problem is finished.

Flowchart

- **IS DIVISOR ALL ZEROS?**
  - YES → **DO NOT DIVIDE**
  - NO ↓
- **ESTABLISH LENGTH OF DIVISOR**
- **DECIDE LENGTH OF QUOTIENT**
- **ADJUST LENGTH OF DIVIDEND**
- **SUBTRACT DIVISOR FROM LEFT SIDE OF DIVIDEND OR FROM REMAINDER**
- **IS RESULT MINUS?**
  - YES → **ADD DIVISOR BACK TO DIVIDEND**
    - **WAS THAT LAST DIGIT IN DIVIDEND?**
      - NO → **BRING DOWN NEXT DIGIT**
      - YES → **FINISH**
  - NO → **ADD ONE TO QUOTIENT**

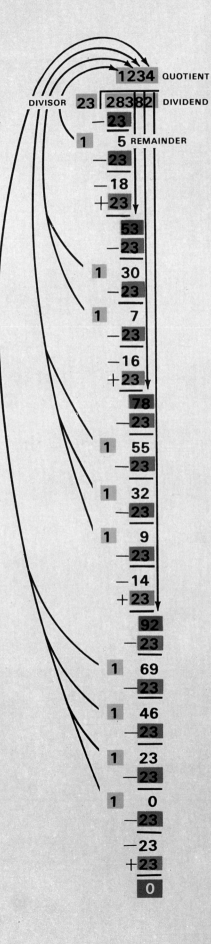

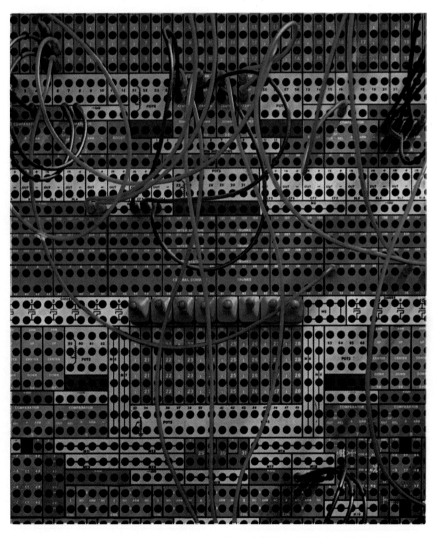

For a Complex "Brain," a Simple Logic

Every problem a computer handles, from long division to analyzing cosmic rays, must first be broken down by a human programmer into simple steps that the computer can solve with its yes-no language of binary notation. The programmer, like the cartoon figure on the page opposite, sets up these steps by plugging wires into holes in the computer's problem board (below). These wires establish a "route of reasoning" along which the problem will travel through the computer. By manipulating the wires, programmers are able to choose different routes for different problems. At left is a diagram of the route for a problem in long division. Every step must be spelled out in detail: a human takes it for granted that when a divisor is zero there can be no division, but a computer takes nothing for granted.

CHARTING A PROBLEM'S ROUTE
A problem board (above) is that part of a computer where wires are the actual physical links that determine the route (schematic diagram opposite) needed for solving a given problem.

Magic Crystals
and a Trend
to Miniatures

In the last few years electronic computers have undergone radical changes. Improved circuits and components not only have enabled them to work much faster but have also made possible a sensational reduction in size. Machines that once filled a great room are now merely crate-sized; and others, designed for spacecraft, can be held in one hand *(below)*.

All this began when scientists discovered that tiny transistors could switch, alter and amplify current far faster than vacuum tubes. Now the new science of microelectronics is replacing transistors with even smaller "monolithic block crystals" *(right)*. Other crystals being developed are so diminutive that one of them, no larger than this capital "O," does the job of four transistors and two resistors.

A HAND-SIZED COMPUTER
Utilizing monolithic crystals, the UNIVAC 1824 *(above)* is a powerful miniature computer. Weighing only 17 pounds, it can be an automatic pilot for a missile, satellite or spaceship.

A HANDFUL OF PARTS
These 16 microelectronic parts *(right)* are made of semiconductors like silicon and germanium, whose molecular structure can be modified to transmit and transmute current in compelling new ways. Some microcircuits are mounted in liquid helium at $-450°$, where there is little resistance to electricity. Etched like a delicate jewel, with no wires to become unsoldered and no tubes to burn out, a single crystal may replace a dozen vacuum tubes and yards of wire.

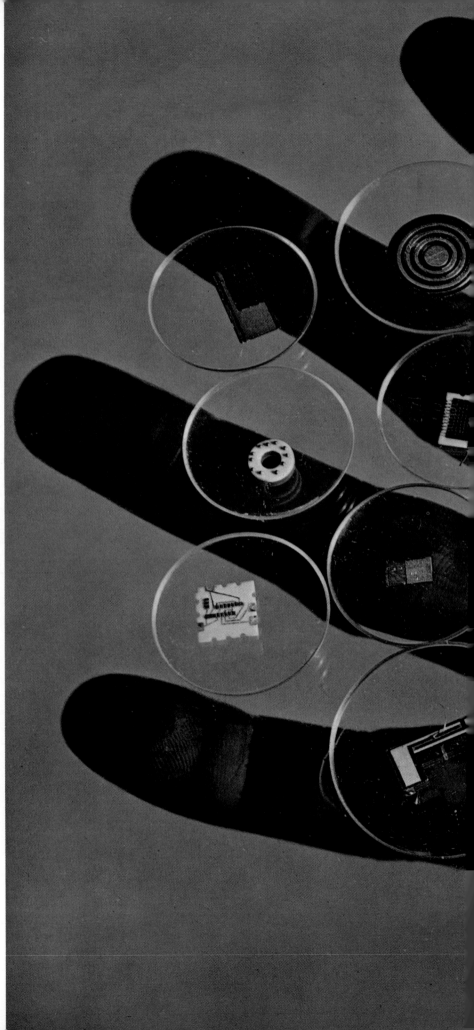

CHESS BY COMPUTER
A chess-playing computer makes its moves on sheets printed with a chessboard pattern *(left)*. The best human players can still beat computers, but possibly not for long: machines are now being programmed to "remember" the consequences of every mistake they have ever made.

THE CURVE OF A PHRASE
A sound engineer studying the problems of building computers that take dictation says "United States" into a mike *(above)*. This creates a unique pattern *(below)* on the screen of an oscilloscope, a machine that transcribes sounds into visible waves. Formerly these waves were in constant motion, but now oscilloscopes can "freeze" them into definite word patterns.

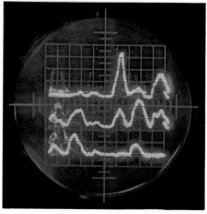

Talented Machines That Act Almost Human

Computers seem to be taking over more and more human functions. They write music, compose poetry, evaluate stock portfolios and even play the intellectual game of chess *(above)*. Experts *(right)* are now trying to make them even more like people by training them to respond to the human voice. One big obstacle is that sound patterns made by people's voices are as distinctive as their fingerprints:

when the computer of the future "hears" a spoken word it will have to weed out those sounds peculiar to the voice, like volume and pitch, and retain only the "pure" phonetic pronunciation of the word. Fears are sometimes expressed that as computers act more and more human "the machines will take over." But computer engineers are not concerned. Says one: "We can always pull the plug."

THE SHAPE OF A WORD
From the oscilloscope pattern of a spoken word *(above)*, engineers can build a three-dimensional plastic model (the one opposite is the word "five"). Such models find the basic sounds of words. Computers can be "taught" to look for these sounds and ignore the speaker's accent.

34

(5) APOLLO - LANDING A MAN

ORBIT of MOON

A COURSE IS CHARTED
Plotting Apollo's first manned moon flight are Dr. Helmut Hoelzer *(left)* and Dr. Rudolph F. Hoelker at the controls of a computer at the Marshall Space Flight Center in Huntsville, Alabama.

Steering Spaceships to the Moon by Computers

The mathematical problems posed by a program to land men on the moon would have been insoluble just over a decade ago. The American moon program—shown here in its five stages—calls for millions of additions and subtractions to calculate effects of the ever-changing gravitational pulls of earth, moon and sun on a rocket in space. To figure out all this with pencil and paper would take human beings centuries. The moon-flight calculations will be made by electronic computers both at ground control centers *(left)* and on the spaceships themselves. These computers will figure the forces acting on a rocket, keep pace with its progress through the heavens, and suggest adjustments for speed and direction. All this is the result of man's learning how to count faster and faster. What began as a way of getting man beyond the number 1 will get him beyond the earth.

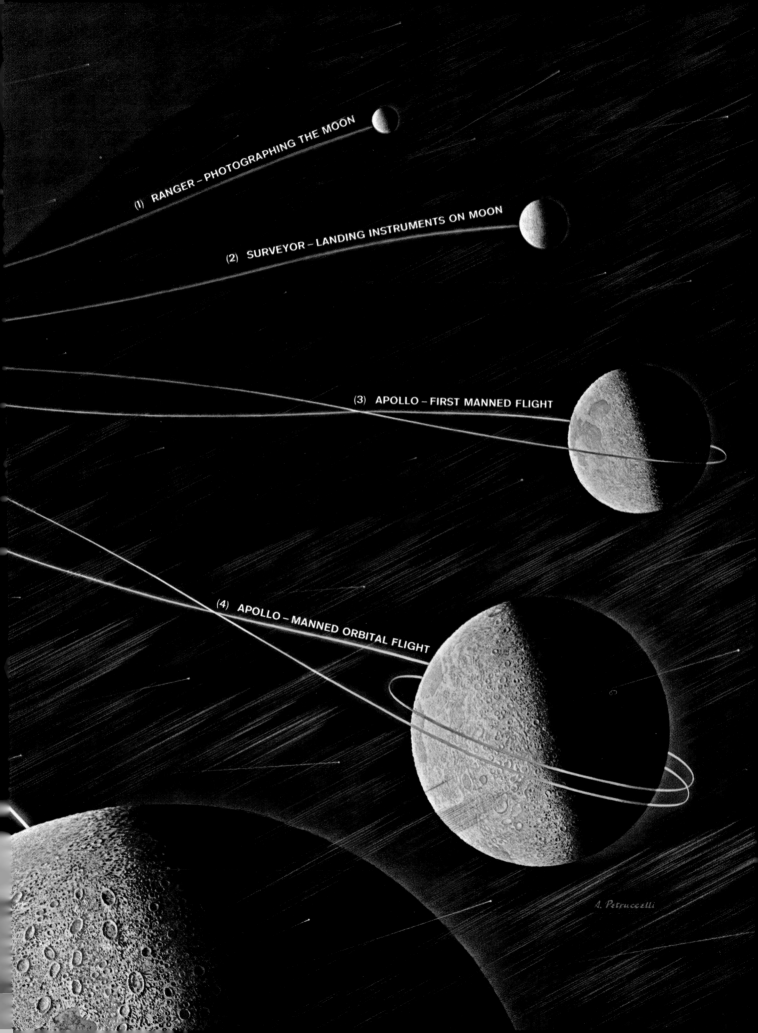

(1) RANGER – PHOTOGRAPHING THE MOON

(2) SURVEYOR – LANDING INSTRUMENTS ON MOON

(3) APOLLO – FIRST MANNED FLIGHT

(4) APOLLO – MANNED ORBITAL FLIGHT

A. Petruccelli

The Shapely
Thinking of the
Ancient Greeks

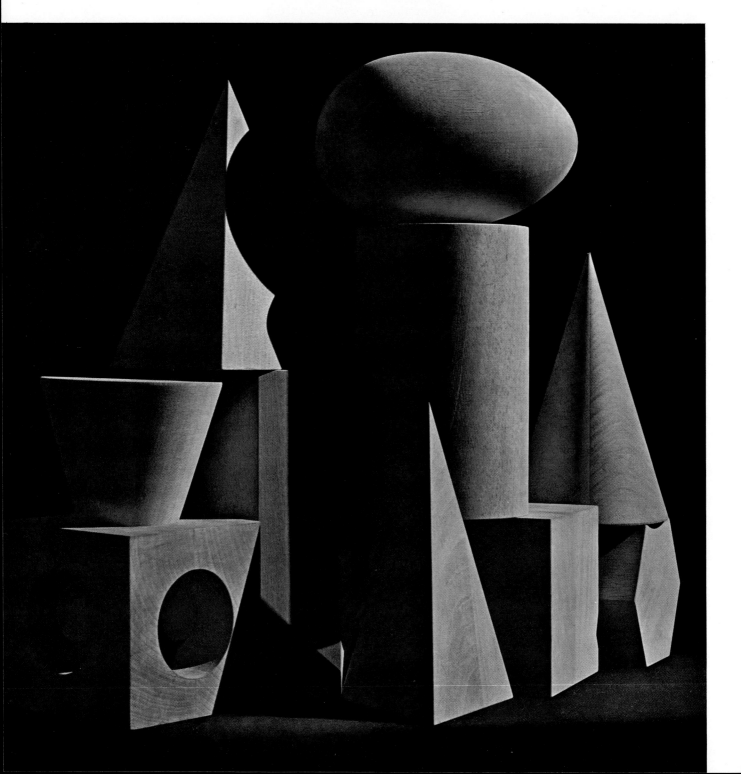

PURE MATHEMATICS—mathematics for its own sake, without any practical goal in mind—began when man first thought of numbers as numbers, apart from the count of his sheep, and when he first thought of shapes as shapes, apart from the turn of a vase. But this early pure mathematics was not the logical, systematic kind that we know today. The forgotten geniuses of Mesopotamia who invented the 60-system seldom paused to ponder the connections between their discoveries or to delve deeply into the thought processes by which they arrived at them. Like the first comers in a rich gold field, they moved from strike to strike, gathering nuggets where they might without digging. The cuneiform tablets and papyrus scrolls on which they and other ancient peoples recorded their mathematical results are as empty of reasoning as cookbook recipes, as niggardly of proofs as drugstore prescriptions. Add this or subtract that, they say, and thou shalt find the truth. One famous Egyptian text, the Rhind Papyrus, describes itself as "directions for knowing all dark things"—rules arranged arbitrarily, and given without explanation.

In the Seventh Century B.C. the ancient Greeks, after 1,000 years of raiding and trading in the eastern Mediterranean, had established a flourishing commerce which exposed them to the accumulated mathematical lore of the older civilizations. They were fascinated and awed by it, but also unsatisfied. Why were the "dark directions" true? With a fresh spirit of skepticism and reason, the Greeks for the first time consciously formulated the two mental processes vital to all mathematical progress: abstraction and proof.

Abstraction is the art of perceiving a common quality or qualities in different things and forming a general idea therefrom. We abstract, for instance, when we see churches, ranch houses and skyscrapers as buildings; when we see cartwheels, automobile tires and hula hoops as circles; when we see cows, cats and dogs as animals.

Proof is the art of arguing from premises to a conclusion in such a way that no flaws can be picked in any step of the argument. The Greeks distinguished between two kinds of premises: general premises, which they called axioms, and more specific premises of mathematics, which they called postulates. But in order to have premises to start with, they invoked another mental process called induction. Whereas abstraction reveals a common denominator in *diverse* things—for instance, cats and dogs are both animals—induction reveals it in the *same class* of things. From our observation of dogs, we make the induction that *all dogs bark;* or from our observation of Doberman pinschers, we induce that *all Doberman pinschers are dogs.* Using the information in these two premises, we can, by a reasoning process known as deduction, prove that *all Doberman pinschers bark.* This inescapable conclusion, or theorem, can also

SOLID ABSTRACTIONS
The Greeks were the first people to pursue mathematics as an art for its own sake. Their invention of pure forms and abstract shapes laid the basis for Euclid's geometry. On the opposite page are some of these forms, whose Greek-derived names we still use: pyramid, cone, prism, hexagon, cylinder and cube.

have a corollary, a statement that necessarily follows from it. A corollary in this case would be: *My neighbor's Doberman pinscher barks.*

The Greeks devised still another technique for achieving a proof, the method which we call by its Latin term *reductio ad absurdum* (reduction to the absurd). Through this we prove the validity of a premise by deliberately assuming the opposite to be true and then demonstrating that this opposite premise cannot stand up. Suppose that Mr. Smith, the neighbor who owns the Doberman pinscher, sets out to examine a complaint that his dog barks constantly. He starts with two premises: that *all dogs are animals* and that *all animals must eat and sleep*. From these he deduces the conclusion that *all dogs must eat and sleep*. He then sets up two more premises: that *some dog barks constantly* (the reverse of what he wishes to prove) and that *dogs that bark constantly cannot eat or sleep*. From this latter set of premises he deduces that *some dog does not eat or sleep*. This conclusion, however, is absurd since it contradicts the earlier one that *all dogs must eat and sleep*. Smith then reexamines all four premises. The only questionable one is that *some dog barks constantly*. Since it led him to an absurd conclusion it must be false, and the opposite of it—that *no dog barks constantly*—must be true. He has thus proved—to his own satisfaction if not to his sleepless neighbor's—what he initially set out to prove.

As may be seen from Smith's mental journey, the principles of Greek proof are really no more than a formalization of the thought processes which we use when trying to present an orderly argument. Smith's way of reasoning is, of course, far less rigorous and less exhaustive than any mathematical reasoning would be. But the mathematician, while conjuring up concepts less palpable than a barking dog, still employs the same basic rules of abstraction and deduction. He abstracts, for instance, when he recognizes that the numbers 6, 52 and 200 can all be divided by 2. He employs *reductio ad absurdum* in examining the premise, say, that an unknown fraction—call it p/q—is a fraction reduced to the lowest terms. If he proves algebraically that each of the unknowns is an even number, he proves his premise "absurd," since a fraction with two even numbers cannot have been reduced to its lowest terms (2/2 or 6/16, for instance, can be further reduced by dividing by 2).

A pyramid of proofs

Prior to the Greeks, mathematicians did not expect anyone to be interested in the mental struggles they had gone through to reach a result —a formula, say, for the amount of stone needed to build a pyramid. If the result worked, that was proof enough of its validity. The Greeks were not merely content to show that a result worked. They wanted to explain why, and this they tried to do by the shortest, strictest logical

THE BEGINNINGS
OF CLASSIC MATHEMATICS

The first Greek to lay down guidelines for the development of geometry in abstract terms, apart from any practical use to which it might be put, was Thales. He enunciated the five simple propositions *(below)* which succeeding eras used as a base for classic mathematics. Thales, incidentally, was an early embodiment of today's geriatrics theory that business retirement need not be boredom. He made his contribution to mathematical thought after amassing a fortune in the marts of free trade.

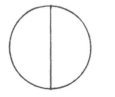

A CIRCLE OF EQUAL HALVES
That a circle is bisected by its diameter was initially demonstrated by Thales, although the early Egyptians may have known of it too.

AN ISOSCELES TRIANGLE
In an isosceles triangle—a triangle that has two equal sides—the two angles that are opposite these sides are equal to each other.

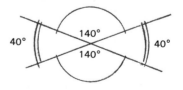

CROSSING STRAIGHT LINES
When two straight lines cross each other, they will form four angles. Of these angles, the ones opposite each other will be equal.

40

argument they could devise. The writing of proofs became an art in which it was a matter of pride to be as economical as possible with the steps in reasoning and yet leave no loopholes. Greek mathematics accumulated a repertory of proved theorems, any one of which could be used without re-proof to formulate some more advanced theorem. Moreover, all the theorems could be arranged, tier upon tier, in an ever-widening inverted pyramid of knowledge. The point at the bottom of the pyramid could be firmly embedded in everyday experience through a few self-evident axioms, such as *the shortest distance between two points is a straight line* or *two straight lines can cross only once*.

As mathematics progressed, the so-called level of rigor—the measure of what constitutes an acceptable formal proof—kept rising, like a water level. As a result, modern mathematicians have found hidden assumptions in some of the Greek proofs. They have even turned up a few limitations in the axiomatic method itself. They have had to devise other sets of axioms on which to construct the newer branches of mathematics. But the basic Greek system of abstraction and proof remains intact. Every branch of modern mathematics, insofar as possible, is organized according to this system.

The moon and a pinhead

The springboard for the Greeks' epochal revolution in thought was geometry. With their natural artistic bent, they were instinctively drawn to the neatness and visual appeal of this mathematics of points, lines, areas and volumes. Both the Babylonians and Egyptians had employed a rough-and-ready geometry in land-surveying and building measurements, but simply as practical applications of counting—in terms, for instance, of the number of tile facings or solid stone blocks required for the west wall of the new palace. The Greeks had a far more abstract approach. They believed that a shape of a certain kind has innate unchanging properties which are independent of its size. Thus, a 45° right triangle—one that has two equal sides—may extend all the way to the moon or it may lie on the head of a pin, but in either case it remains a 45° right triangle.

The first Greek to grasp this fundamental possibility for abstraction in geometry—and to glimpse the Greek dream that knowledge would rise in solid inverted pyramids of proof from a few elementary axioms—was probably Thales of Miletus, an enterprising olive-oil tycoon who operated along the coasts of Asia Minor from about 600 to 550 B.C. In his travels he had come in contact with the lore of the old mathematics and astronomy, and in his retirement he took them up as a hobby. The five propositions which he is credited with demonstrating—seen in the margins below—were so simple as to indicate that he was consciously trying

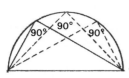

ANGLES IN A SEMICIRCLE
Any angle inscribed within a semicircle is a right angle (one of 90°). Thales sacrificed a bull, it is said, in joy over this discovery.

CONGRUENT TRIANGLES
Two triangles are congruent—equal in all respects—if they contain two angles and one side that respectively equal each other.

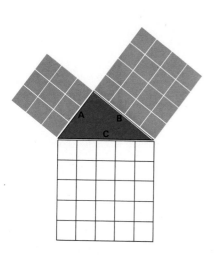

RENOWNED THEOREM AT WORK
Best grasped in diagrammatic form, the most famous Pythagorean teaching is that the square on the long side of a right triangle (C) equals the sum of the squares on the short sides (A and B). Assuming that A, B and C are respectively 3, 4 and 5 feet long, we can find the square of C—25 square feet—by adding together the squares of A and B (9 square feet plus 16 square feet).

to establish the foundations of geometry in unshakably basic terms.

Thales' ambition might have remained unfulfilled had it not been for another Greek who, it is believed, studied with him. This was Pythagoras, a man of magnetic and forceful personality. Legend has it that at Thales' recommendation Pythagoras spent years in travel, seeking to enlarge his mathematical understanding. Among the sources he is said to have tapped were the priests of Zoroaster—the wise men, or Magi, of the Christmas story—who had become custodians of Mesopotamian mathematical lore under the Persian Empire. Then, having learned all he could, Pythagoras about 540 B.C. founded a semireligious, semimathematical cult in Crotona, a burgeoning Greek colonial town on the instep of the Italian boot. Along with mathematics, he taught his disciples to worship numbers; to believe in reincarnation and the transmigration of souls from man to man and man to beast; never to eat beans; always to remain anonymous and sign the name of the Pythagorean brotherhood to any writing or discovery.

The best-remembered of the Pythagorean teachings is, of course, the theorem that in a right triangle the square on the long side—the hypotenuse—is equal to the sum of the squares on the two shorter sides. The Babylonians had discovered this theorem a millennium earlier, but the Pythagorean school is credited as the first to prove it. It is still tremendously useful in science. But what is of more down-to-earth interest for most of us, carpenters depend on the principle behind the theorem to make sure that the rooms they lay out are perfect rectangles.

Legacy for a jazz pianist

Pythagoras made a second highly practical contribution, which figures in every performance by a jazz pianist or string quartet. This was his discovery of the underlying mathematics of the musical scale. Pythagoras found that a marvelous connection existed between musical harmony and the whole numbers we count by—1, 2, 3, 4, 5 and so on. Pluck a string and sound a note, then pluck an equally taut string twice as long and you hear a new note just one harmonic octave below the first. Starting with any string and the note it sounds, you can go down the scale by increasing the length of the string according to simple fractions expressible as the ratios of whole numbers. For instance, 16/15 of a C-string gives the next lower note B, 6/5 of it gives A, 4/3 of it gives G, 3/2 of it gives F, 8/5 of it gives E, 16/9 of it gives D, and exactly two of it give C again, an octave lower. Pythagoras discovered the whole-number relationships between C, F, G and low C and between their equivalents in any scale. From this find he progressed to the firm conviction that all harmony, all beauty, all nature can be expressed by whole-number relationships. He even believed that the planets, as they move in their orbits, must give off a heavenly whole-numbered harmony—the so-called "music of the spheres."

So enraptured were the Pythagoreans by the peerless power of the integers, so certain were they that the entire universe was made up of these whole numbers, that they took to classifying them into categories such as "perfect" and "amicable." They also labeled the even numbers as feminine and the odd numbers as masculine—excepting only the number 1, which they regarded as the generator of all the numbers. (The symbol for marriage was the number 5, the sum of the first feminine number, 2, and the first masculine number, 3.) Then, in the wake of this charming fantasy, a sobering discovery was made, one so un-Pythagorean that the brotherhood tried to suppress it.

Mischief in a square root

The disturbing find was a new kind of number—one which we today call an "irrational." The characteristic of the irrational is that it remains stubbornly unwhole no matter what. This maddening trait turns up frequently in what we call a square root—the quantity which, when multiplied by itself, produces the given number. The square root of 4 (symbolically written as $\sqrt{4}$) is a neat, tidy 2; $\sqrt{9}$ is 3. But an irrational square root turns out to be a decimal fraction with an endless series of nonrepeating digits after the decimal point. For example, $\sqrt{2}$ is 1.41421 . . . and so on ad infinitum, $\sqrt{3}$ is 1.73205 . . . ad infinitum. Even more unsettling to the orderly mind, irrational square roots crop up with dismaying frequency.

The case of the right triangle will serve as an example. A right triangle whose short sides are three and four units long and whose whole hypotenuse is an even five units long is very exceptional. For every one of its kind—every 3-4-5, 5-12-13 or 7-24-25 triangle—there are innumerable "imperfect" right triangles with sides like $1\text{-}1\text{-}\sqrt{2}$ or $1\text{-}2\text{-}\sqrt{5}$ or $2\text{-}\sqrt{5}\text{-}3$. Suppose you are measuring a field laid out in the form of a right triangle with two equal sides and a third long side. Suppose the two equal sides come out evenly in feet. Then the third side will not come out evenly—no matter if you measure it in microcaliper fractions of an inch or centimeter—or if you start all over again to measure in cubits or furlongs. No matter how many times you subdivide the length of the long side, you will never come out with a subdivision that equals a subdivision of the length of either short side. Between the long and either of the short sides there is no common measure whatsoever.

The Pythagoreans realized that in most right triangles the irreducible ratios between the lengths of the sides could not be expressed in terms of whole numbers, not even if all the whole numbers and all their fractions—from 1 to a trillion or from 1/1 to a trillionth—were called into

A TEST OF BELLS AND WATER

A TEST OF STRING TENSIONS

A TEST OF COLUMNS OF AIR

A PHILOSOPHER OF MANY PARTS
These 15th Century Italian woodcuts imagine Pythagoras proving his ideas of harmony by various tests on bells and on glasses of water *(top)*, on string tensions *(middle)* and on lengths of columns of air *(bottom)*.

A MATHEMATICS OF MUSIC
Pythagoras found that musical intervals are governed by ratios of whole numbers, as seen on the C-string superimposed on an old violin engraving. Finger position I produces a length of string that gives low C, an octave below middle C; II, 3/4 of length, gives F above low C; III, 2/3 of length, gives G; IV, 1/2 the length, gives middle C.

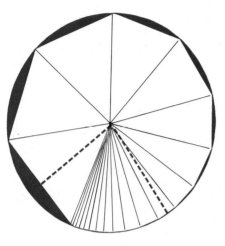

SIZING UP A CIRCLE
The smaller the triangles that are inscribed within a circle, the more nearly they fill it up, shown by the diminishing colored areas above. Moreover, as these triangles shrink, their height *(dotted line)* gets closer to the length of the radius and their bases nearly sit on the circumference. Seeing that height became radius and that the sum of the bases equaled the circumference, the Greeks applied the formula for a triangle's area (1/2 base × height) to the formula for a circle's area (1/2 circumference × radius).

service for the attempt. This crushing discovery affected the entire course of Greek mathematical thinking. It effectively dashed any hope that measurement might be used as a bridge between geometry and the arithmetic of whole numbers. The Greeks began to restrict themselves to shape-geometry, which concerned itself not with measurement but only with shape. They could thus draw, if not measure, certain irrational numbers, such as $\sqrt{2}$ or $\sqrt{3}$, as a definite hypotenuse in a definite right triangle. Like rambunctious children, these could at least be corralled within definitely bordered rectilinear figures—triangles, squares and pyramids.

But neither irrationals nor the concept of infinity would stay out of even the most elementary shape-geometry. After triangles, both cropped up again in the problem of the circle. The ratio of a circle's circumference to its diameter is itself an irrational number, 3.14159 . . ., which we call pi, or symbolically π. (It is believed that the first letter of the Greek word *periphereia*—meaning "periphery"—inspired the π symbol. Whatever its origin, the quantity it represents has been calculated to more than 100,000 decimal places, and we know that it will never come out evenly.) The Greeks did not recognize the full extent of π's irrationality, and so they wasted much labor trying to solve the one big problem which this fact made impossible—constructing a square whose area is equal to that of a given circle, or literally trying to "square the circle."

Infinity and apple pie

The best way they could assess the area of a circle itself was as the sum of an infinite number of infinitely narrow triangles ranged around the center of the circle like so many stingy slivers of apple pie. The height of each infinitely narrow triangle was the same as the radius of the circle. The sum of the infinitely short bases of all the triangles was the same as the circumference of the circle. And since the combined area of all the triangles should equal half their height times the sum of their bases, the area of the circle should equal half its radius times its circumference. There was nothing wrong with this conclusion. It worked. But trying to prove it by rigorous step-by-step logic was an intellectual journey as arduous as the odyssey of Ulysses. As a triangle becomes infinitely narrow, exactly when does it cease to be ◄-shaped and start to behave as if it were a ◄-shaped sliver of pie? Surely it does not take on the shape of a proper pie-slice until it is infinitely narrow and then, surely, it is no longer something but nothing. How can an infinite number of nothings be added up to produce a something such as a circle?

These troublesome objections to the logic of fine-slicing a circle were posed—probably with glee—by the Eleatic school of philosophers, a school which had come into being at Elea, next door to Crotona and the

Pythagoreans. From the start the Eleatics seem to have opposed the Pythagoreans. Mathematics was no mere pastime for the Greeks; its problems were fought out in an open arena. What in retrospect seems a serene and unimpeded parade of progress toward greater knowledge was, in fact, an intellectual war waged with all the fervor of a wineshop controversy. The weapons of this war were sophisticated arguments. Its ultimate prize was the triumph of proof.

The Eleatics were deeply interested in scientific understanding—not just of triangles and circles but of the whole cosmos. Their leading spokesman was Zeno, master of that perplexing device, the paradox—a proposition which, though valid logically, flies in the face of common sense. Zeno was fascinated by the idea of infinity. He rightly felt that science could not grapple with reality unless it took into account the ways infinity seems to appear everywhere in nature. He posed a simple question involving motion and propounded a now-celebrated paradox. How is it possible for a moving point to pass through an infinite number of positions in a finite time? If the fleet-footed Achilles runs a race with a tortoise and the tortoise is given as much as a foot's head start, how can Achilles—by rigorous Greek logic—ever catch up? When Achilles has gone a foot, the tortoise has also trudged ahead by, say, a tenth of a foot. And when Achilles has covered the tenth, the tortoise is still some farther distance on its way.

Anyone knows from experience that Achilles can catch up with the tortoise, but how does anyone prove it by logical steps that do not need an infinity of pages for the proving? Modern mathematicians have ways of sidestepping the problem and so did the Greeks. One of the early sages of geometry, probably Eudoxus, supplemented the controversial proof about the area of a circle with two subsidiary lines of reasoning. These showed that if the area of a circle is more or less than half its circumference times its radius, contradictions arise—contradictions which reduce the alternatives to absurdities (thus, again, *reductio ad absurdum*).

At about the same time that Eudoxus was scoring this point over the Eleatics and infinity, the old Greek world was being swallowed up in the almost infinite conquests of Alexander the Great. When the clangor of arms had subsided, a new capital of Greek culture emerged at Alexandria in Egypt. And there, about 300 B.C., the most famous of all masters of geometry, Euclid, set out to collect the theorems of his predecessors and to arrange them as a single self-contained whole.

Euclid was not himself a great innovator, but he was a superb organizer of the mathematical results achieved by Thales, Eudoxus and other luminaries of the golden age of Greek geometry—men who are no more than names to us now, such as Democritus, Hippocrates of Chios, and Archytas. Euclid was eminently skilled at rewriting their proofs in

SERVING UP A PARADOX
Zeno confounded his fellow thinkers mightily by pointing out that the heroic Achilles, no matter how fast he ran, could not overtake a crawling tortoise with a head start, since when he reached the tortoise's starting point, A, the tortoise would have moved ahead to B. When he got to B the tortoise would have moved ahead to C. In this wise, Zeno argued, the tortoise would always be out in front, even if by a mere eyelash.

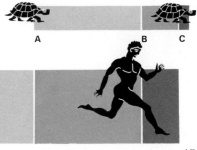

EUCLID'S AXIOMS

*Things equal to the same thing
are equal.*

*If equals are added to equals,
the sums are equal.*

*If equals are subtracted from
equals, the remainders are equal.*

*Things which coincide with one
another are equal to one another.*

*The whole is greater than
the part.*

EUCLID'S POSTULATES

*A straight line can be drawn
from any point to any other point.*

*A finite straight line can be
drawn continuously in a straight line.*

*A circle can be described with
any point as center, and with a radius
equal to any finite straight line
drawn from the center.*

*All right angles are equal to
each other.*

*Given a straight line and any
point not on this line, there is,
through that point, one and only one
line that is parallel to the given line.*

terse, clear terms. Thus simplified, they are contained in his masterpiece, the *Elements,* one of those unique books like the Bible which seem to fuse the best efforts of generations of creative minds into a single inspired whole. It is a work of such commanding lucidity and style that some scholars consider it the most coherent collection of closely reasoned thoughts ever set down by man. In antiquity it was circulated widely in manuscript form. Since the invention of printing, a thousand editions of it have been published. Until about a century ago it was the standard high-school text on geometry throughout most of the world. Today, in various rewritten forms, it still is.

The *Elements* contains 13 books, or chapters, which describe and prove a good part of all that the human race knows, even now, about lines, points, circles and the elementary solid shapes. All this information Euclid deduced, by the most mind-sharpening logic, from just 10 simple premises—five postulates and five axioms (set forth in the margin at the left). Out of these premises Euclid constructed not only the geometry normally taught today in high school but also a great deal of other mathematics. His chapters on line lengths and areas give geometric methods for solving many problems that are now taken up as algebra. His handling of the Zeno-plagued concept of infinity and of the technique for summing up areas under circular arcs involves ideas now studied in calculus. His discussion of prime numbers—numbers which cannot be evenly divided except by themselves or by 1—is now a classic of college-level "number theory."

After Euclid, mathematicians could only go up—out of the realms normally thought of as Greek geometry into the rarefied atmosphere of what is popularly known as higher mathematics. Inspired by the *Elements,* the two most gifted mathematicians of the next century were to originate as many new results and generate as many useful formulas as all the pre-Euclidean Greeks put together. One was Apollonius, whose discoveries about the so-called conic sections later contributed importantly to astronomy, to the military science of ballistics and finally to modern rocketry. The other was Archimedes, whose brilliance at mathematics was matched by a genius for mechanics which made him the father of practical engineering.

Plato's blessing and ban

So far as possible, both Apollonius and Archimedes conducted their higher mathematical researches within the rigorous discipline imposed on geometry by the renowned Athenian philosopher Plato. Because he thought in terms of the pure ideal, the totally abstract, Plato was devoted to geometry; he liked the way it could abstract from a bumpy cart wheel to the concept of a circle immune from time and change. Because of his prestige, he was able to communicate his enthusiasm to his fellow citizens, thereby giving the practitioners of geometry a high place in public esteem. But while conferring this cachet upon them, he also saddled them with a difficult work restriction. Frowning, philosopherlike, upon mere mechanical discovery and applied mathematics, Plato insisted that geometric proofs be demonstrated with no aids other than a straightedge and a compass. This requirement, which did not originate with Plato but took stimulus from him, applied across the board to all elementary geometric problems and when feasible to advanced problems.

(Both because of his lofty approach to mathematics and the straightedge-and-compass regulation, some mathematicians still regard Plato with a leery eye. The great 19th Century British logician Augustus De Morgan noted caustically that the words which Plato supposedly inscribed over the gates of his academy—"Let no man ignorant of geometry enter"—no more indicated that geometry existed within the gates than "a warning not to forget to bring a packet of sandwiches would . . . give promise of a good dinner.")

Apollonius made his contribution to mathematical history by investigating all the most important quirks of a series of graceful curves which he described in a book entitled *Conics*. He called them conics because he visualized them as cuts made by a flat or plane surface when it intersects the surface of a cone; it was as if he mentally took a hack saw to an ice cream cone. Depending on how the cone was cut, the resulting dissections were circles, ellipses, parabolas or hyperbolas. (Some of these are shown at the right.) Then he investigated the properties of each conic cut and showed how they are all interrelated. As pure mathematics all these ingenious labors need no justification, but they have turned out to be doubly justified by the fact that conic sections are the paths which projectiles, satellites, moons or earths follow under the influence of gravity around planets or stars.

Apollonius' rival and friend was Archimedes, who was a little more brilliant and a great deal more creative—so much so that within the profession he is ranked, with Newton and Gauss, as one of the three great mathematicians of all time. Everything that Archimedes did seems as modern in spirit today as when he created it. Yet he created all that he did within the narrow bounds of Platonic discipline, without any algebraic shorthand to catalyze his logic and without even a convenient system of notation for writing large numbers and doing complicated arithmetic.

Most Greeks had no simple way of writing really large numbers. Archimedes faced up to this severe disadvantage in a scientific treatise, the *Sand Reckoner*, setting forth a system of numbers based on the Greek myriad, or 10,000. Numbers up to a myriad of myriads, or 100 million, he

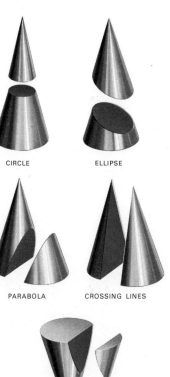

CIRCLE   ELLIPSE

PARABOLA   CROSSING LINES

HYPERBOLA

THE CONIC CUTS OF APOLLONIUS
Apollonius found that certain curves, or conics, resulted if a flat plane intersected a circular cone in various ways. A cut parallel to the cone's base made a circle; an oblique cut an ellipse. A slice parallel to a line on the cone made a parabola, like a projectile's path. A cut down through the top point produced two intersecting lines. Slicing through the cone and the mirror image atop it resulted in a hyperbola, or double curve like a lamp shade's shadow.

called "the first order of numbers." Numbers up to a myriad of myriads multiplied by themselves a myriad myriad times—$100,000,000^{100,000,000}$ — he called "numbers of the first period." He went on to let this enormous number be multiplied by itself a myriad myriad times, arriving at a quantity so vast that in 10-system notation it would be written as a 1 followed by 80 million billion zeros. This impressive cavalcade, he pointed out, is a quite adequate number.

The case of the countless cattle

Large numbers held so few terrors for Archimedes' unfettered mind that, the story goes, he was able to tease fellow mathematicians with one of the most horrendous mathematical riddles ever posed. "If thou art diligent and wise, O stranger, compute the number of cattle of the sun, who once upon a time grazed on the fields of the Thrinacian isle of Sicily." By "cattle of the sun" Archimedes meant those belonging to Hyperion, the sun-god, and in straight-faced fashion he went on to describe the herd and the various colors of cows and bulls in it. Because of a slightly ambiguous wording, the problem he posed turned out to have two possible answers. Either the cattle number 5,916,837,175,686, or they can be counted only by a 206,545-digit number, which no one, not even the stouthearted Archimedes, has ever had the longevity to work out. And it is quite possible that this was the whole point of his joke.

The achievement of which Archimedes himself was most proud was the discovery of how to calculate the volume of a sphere. He found that the volume of a sphere equals two thirds the volume of the smallest possible cylinder which will enclose it. (At his request, the sphere-and-cylinder diagram with which he worked was graven on his tombstone when he died in 212 B.C. and was freed from overgrowing vines and grime by the Roman orator Cicero when he made a pilgrimage to the forgotten grave a century and a half later.) To show that a cylinder is half again as voluminous as its "inscribed sphere," Archimedes had to apply the same technique of infinite fine-slicing that earlier Greeks had used on the area of a circle. Then he had to prove by the method of *reductio ad absurdum* that if more or less than two thirds of the circumscribing cylinder equaled the volume of the sphere, the results would lead to contradiction. He employed the same technique to demonstrate what areas were enclosed within parabolic curves and certain spiral curves. He used it again to compute the volume of space which a conic section sweeps out as it rotates on its axis.

Because of his practical turn of mind, Archimedes was a physicist and engineer as well as a mathematician. Many who know little else about him remember him as a sort of absent-minded professor who ran

ARENA OF GREEK MATHEMATICS
Places linked with mathematical luminaries of ancient Greece are, going from west to east, Syracuse (Archimedes), Elea (Zeno), Crotona (Pythagoras), Miletus (Thales) and Alexandria (Euclid, Apollonius, Hypatia).

naked through the streets of the Sicilian city of Syracuse, where he lived, crying, "Eureka, Eureka!"—meaning "I have found it!" What he had actually found was a physicist's fact, a basic law of hydraulic engineering. Any bath-taker is aware that a solid sunk in a liquid displaces its own *volume* of that liquid. But Archimedes discovered that a solid floating on a liquid displaces its own *weight* of that liquid and in general that a solid immersed in a liquid loses exactly as much weight as the weight of the water it pushes aside.

How Archimedes became involved in this problem was later explained by the Roman architect Vitruvius. King Hieron of Syracuse, who had provided one of his court jewelers with gold to make a crown for him, suspected that silver had been substituted for some of the gold. He engaged his friend Archimedes as sleuth. Archimedes was pondering the problem one day, floating in his bath—with his own weight in water spilling over the edges of the tub—when he first realized his hydraulic law. From this discovery and through the use of some geometric algebra, he was able to find out how much adulterating silver the goldsmith had used. Possibly he demonstrated the fraud by weighing out amounts of gold and silver equal to the weight of the crown, first in air and then in water. Whichever way he closed the case, Hieron was hugely satisfied and the court jeweler hugely chagrined—or worse.

Archimedes' detective work on crowns and hydraulics was a mere fraction of his contribution to practical engineering. His celebrated declaration, "Give me a place to stand and I will move the earth," stemmed not from boastfulness but from excitement at having found proofs of the mathematical laws of the lever. He also discovered the laws of pulleys and methods of finding the center of gravity of an object—all principles which are still standbys in erecting a skyscraper or throwing a bridge over a river. How skillfully he could apply his own discoveries can be judged from the fact—reported by Plutarch and others—that he held an invading Roman fleet at bay in Syracuse harbor for three years with devastating catapults and big-beaked, ship-biting iron claws of his own design. The Roman general Marcellus, after his first repulse, called Archimedes "this geometrical Briareus [a mythological monster with a hundred arms] who uses our ships like cups to ladle water from the sea."

Aftermath of a bacchanal

Unfortunately for the Syracusans, Marcellus eventually outmaneuvered the Archimedean versions of the ultimate weapon by stealing up on an ill-guarded turret of the city wall at night during one of their periodic religious bacchanals. At daybreak the invaders presented the city with a hangover of murder and pillage. Contrary to Marcellus' specific orders, a Roman soldier, on finding Archimedes bemusedly drawing

SOME PAST VOGUES IN SYMBOLIC SHORTHAND

Just as our present symbols for add, subtract, multiply and divide had their precursors (shown on page 11), so other shorthand signs in use today had their onetime variations. The symbols we employ for square root, cube root and pi— $\sqrt{\ }$, $\sqrt[3]{\ }$ and π —appear starkly simple by comparison with versions devised in past eras by mathematicians embarked on flights of artistic whim and fancy.

A SQUARE-ROOT SIGN
This sign is from *radix* (Latin for root) and was first used by Leonardo da Pisa in 1220. Today's $\sqrt{\ }$ sign, which may be a distortion of the letter "r," is 16th Century German.

A CUBE-ROOT SIGN
Three modern-style radical signs run together, this symbol was created in 1525 by Christoff Rudolff, the German mathematician. Today's $\sqrt[3]{\ }$ sign was 17th Century French in origin.

ANOTHER SIGN FOR PI
This alternative to our present symbol for pi was proposed by Professor Benjamin Peirce of Harvard in 1859. Today's π sign, a Greek letter, was launched in England in the 1700s.

geometric figures in the sand of a courtyard, cut the old man down. Archimedes was 75 at the time, and it probably did not matter much to him. But had he been spared, he conceivably might have lit the candle of creativity in a Roman or two. Instead his death signaled the onset of an intellectual blight which was to ravage the world for centuries, and was ultimately to send the Greeks' prodigious brainchild, geometry, to an untimely grave.

The Romans took over the war machines and engineering of Archimedes, but they left his wellspring of original mathematics totally untapped. During imperial Rome's mental, spiritual and physical debauch over the next centuries, a few badgered Greeks did their best to preserve the Archimedean tradition of creative inquiry. Among the last of them was the beautiful, immensely learned woman mathematician Hypatia, who lectured at the University of Alexandria about 400 A.D. and attracted students by droves. Unfortunately she was one of the last of the pagan Greek intellectuals and was killed by a sectarian Christian mob. Edward Gibbon described her end in *The Decline and Fall of the Roman Empire:* she was "torn from her chariot, stripped naked, dragged to the church" and there "her flesh was scraped from her bones with sharp oyster shells and her quivering limbs were delivered to the flames."

Long adying, Greek mathematics had now gasped its last. Another 1,000 years were to pass before its spirit blazed up again.

A Portfolio:
Eminent Masters
of Mathematics

Mathematicians frequently are lone researchers into the most abstruse matters, but frequently they work with other scientists. They help guide spaceships through the heavens, inquire into the nature of communication, unlock the secrets of genetics. As individuals, mathematicians seem to share certain characteristics. They are usually very young in their most productive years, sometimes in their teens. Some use mathematics whimsically, to compose 12-tone melodies that sound the same played forward or backward, or set computers to writing avant-garde blank verse. Others are fascinated by gadgets. Claude Shannon *(opposite)* invented a startling black box which, when its engine starts up, opens to let a green hand snake out and turn itself off. Here and on the following pages, in photographs by Alfred Eisenstaedt, are portraits of some distinguished practitioners in the U.S. of the mathematician's arcane and indispensable art.

COMMUNICATION THEORIST
Standing before the flashing lights of a computer at the Massachusetts Institute of Technology is Professor Claude Shannon. He uses Boolean algebra to design telephone switching circuits and is the inventor of information theory—which may show science how to simulate the workings of the human brain. He has also created an electronic mouse that can find its way out of a maze.

"Pure" Mathematicians: Practitioners of an Elegant Art

There are now 38,000 mathematicians in America. This total is not enough to meet the demand. Happily, enrollment in higher mathematics in some universities is increasing 30 per cent annually. Of some 600 creative "pure" mathematicians now working in the U.S., many were educated in Europe, including Kurt Gödel and Samuel Eilenberg, who are shown here.

The only thing that interests these men is extending the borders of men's mathematical knowledge. They pay no attention to the practical application of their research. They see their work as an art and judge its value by the brilliance and beauty of its logic, the elegance of its reasoning. Mathematical elegance, as one of these men has put it, is "directly proportional to the number of ideas you can see in it and inversely proportional to the effort it takes to see them." Thus the pure mathematicians have developed geometries of both infinite dimension and no particular dimension—and they have proved that in certain respects mathematics is not subject to proof at all.

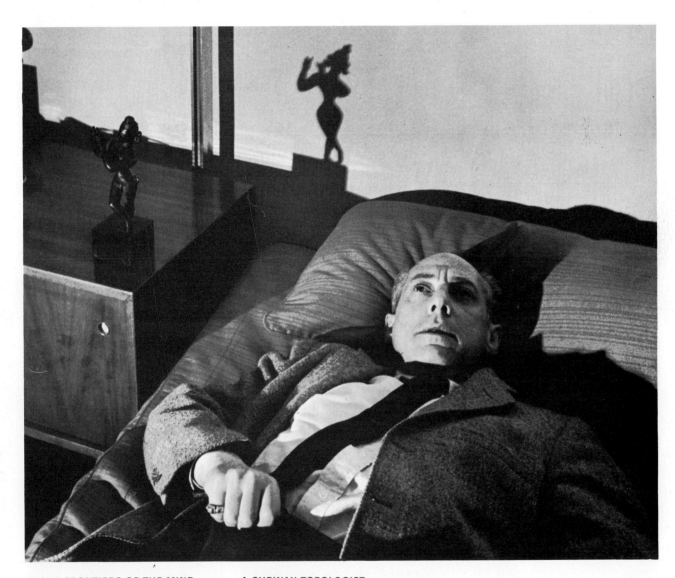

AT THE FRONTIERS OF THE MIND
One of the most renowned mathematicians in the U.S. is Dr. Kurt Gödel, who stands *(opposite)* in the library of the Institute for Advanced Study in Princeton, New Jersey. Born in Czechoslovakia, he achieved his first fame at 25. Scholars had suggested the existence of absolute guides to the truth or falsity of certain mathematical statements. Gödel shocked his elders by proving that what they sought did not exist. He is now examining the implications of this finding. "Either mathematics is too big for the human mind," he says, "or the human mind is more than a machine." He hopes to prove the latter.

A SUBWAY TOPOLOGIST
Chairman of the Department of Mathematics at Columbia University, Polish-born Professor Samuel Eilenberg sprawls contemplatively in his Greenwich Village apartment in New York City. "Sometimes I like to think lying down," he says, "but mostly I like to think riding on the subway." Mainly he thinks about algebraic topology—a field so abstruse that even among mathematicians few understand it. Eilenberg is the first non-French member of Bourbaki, a semisecret group of scholars which is engaged in publishing a monumental compendium of abstract mathematics under the name of the fictitious "Nicholas Bourbaki."

Specialists
in Putting the Abstract
to Work

Applied mathematicians bring the abstractions of pure mathematics back down to earth. Stating real physical problems in mathematical terms, they frequently turn yesterday's pure equations into today's industrial schedules, actuarial tables or voting forecasts. Sometimes the mathematical solution to a seemingly unmathematical problem has more than a single application: one equation can describe both the diffusion of blood in the kidneys and the diffusion of atoms in a reactor.

A number of pure mathematicians profess to look down upon their more practical colleagues; reflecting this, only four U.S. universities support departments of applied mathematics. Nevertheless, many graduates in pure mathematics have put their skills to practical use: about half of all U.S. mathematicians work in industry. Their handiwork ranges from designing automobiles to probing the vagaries of human nature.

Using new branches of mathematics such as game and information theory, these experts are bringing major changes in business and military tactics, communications and medicine. Their work has begun to suggest that no area of human endeavor is beyond mathematics' reach.

A GENETIC STATISTICIAN
A mathematical geneticist at the University of Pittsburgh's School of Public Health, Professor Ching Chun Li looks at a slide showing chromosome aberrations in the cells of an infant. From statistical analysis of such material, Dr. Li is able to determine facts about human populations that cannot be found through experiment.

TESTING BY TENSION
One of the founders of Brown University's Department of Applied Mathematics is precise and formal Professor William Prager (right), whose specialty is the mechanics of solids. In front of him is the "universal testing machine," which checks the strength of metals by subjecting them to tremendous pull.

Mathematicians as Public Servants and Missionaries

The men shown on these pages are exceptions to the general rule that creative mathematicians are rarely public-spirited. Most scientists in their field feel that anything that takes them away from their desks and quiet offices interrupts their principal task, which is the creation of mathematics. Group research bores them, forums repel them, politics horrifies them and even teaching often annoys them.

Prominent among the exceptions to the rule are several men serving the federal government in important jobs. These include Brockway MacMillan, an assistant secretary of defense, and Professor John Tukey (opposite), who serves on the President's Science Advisory Committee. There are others who head up major research institutions.

Among those most dedicated to public service are teachers like Professor David Blackwell (at left), who teaches advanced statistics and dynamic programming at the University of California. An enthusiastic classroom educator, Dr. Blackwell

makes lecture tours which are sponsored by the Mathematical Association of America in order to help ignite sparks of interest in his subject.

Professor John Kemeny (below), chairman of the Department of Mathematics at Dartmouth College, also travels around the country urging youngsters to study mathematics. He has so successfully argued that "the man ignorant of mathematics will be increasingly limited in his grasp of the main forces of civilization" that an amazing 90 per cent of the students on his campus are taking elective courses in mathematics.

Ironically, just as the demand for more teachers is mounting, the colleges and universities have been trying to free men for research by reducing their teaching loads. Old schedules of 12 to 14 hours of teaching weekly have been cut to nine and even six hours. Thus one of the most critical problems in mathematics today is how to train more students in the fewer hours of teaching time now available.

COFFEE-BREAK LECTURER

David Blackwell, an inspired teacher in the University of California's mathematical statistics department, presides over an impromptu seminar that boiled up around a blackboard during a morning coffee break. In research he applies probability analysis and statistical studies to "the search problem"—to learn, for example, how best to find a cancer-curing drug among a vast number of chemical possibilities. Despite his need, as a teacher, to communicate with others, Dr. Blackwell keeps no telephone at home—because he has eight children, each with his own need for communication with friends.

PRESIDENTIAL ADVISER

Though he is easygoing and relaxed, Professor John Tukey *(above)* is one of the nation's busiest mathematicians. A former chemist who got his Ph.D. in mathematics, he now specializes in statistics and spends a day or so each week in Washington, where he serves on a number of advisory committees. The rest of his week is divided between the Department of Mathematics at Princeton University and the Bell Laboratories at nearby Murray Hill, New Jersey. He was photographed at the Bell computer lab working on his Citation Index, a growing catalogue of sources in the fields of statistics and probability.

MATHEMATICS MISSIONARY

Teaching Dartmouth freshmen, Professor John Kemeny demonstrates how to use calculus to determine the value of pi to a desired number of decimal places. Soft-voiced and gentle, with a gift for making the abstruse sound amusing, he thinks dull teaching causes most people to shy away from mathematics. He is greatly concerned because industry is draining away many of the bright new Ph.D.s in mathematics and the shortage of good teachers is likely to persist. So he travels restlessly up and down the land, scouting the high schools like a football coach, looking for good mathematics recruits.

Navigators
Charting Courses
to Outer Space

Aside from universities, the Department of Defense and the aircraft and electronics industries are the chief employers of mathematicians in the United States. One important field in which they work is celestial exploration: mathematicians—like the two shown here—must do the spadework for the space race. For a single space flight, they must compute about 100 trajectories, then choose the best one—plus another 20 or so alternatives for emergencies. Among the myriad factors they have to deal with are the possibilities of collision with meteorites, the safest routes through radiation, and the weight and rate of expenditure of fuel. The actual figuring of each trajectory takes a computer a matter of seconds—but only after five people have worked four or five months to feed it the correct information.

Not until the mathematicians are finished can the engineers proceed with the construction of spacecraft and launching of flights. The importance of mathematics was underscored in the first Mariner flight toward Venus. A minute typographical slip in one mathematical equation that was fed into a computer ruined the entire flight—the $18.5 million Mariner went off course and had to be destroyed.

A PERFECTER OF QUESTIONS

Poring over figures in the computer laboratory *(right)* is the RAND Corporation's athletic Dr. Richard Bellman, who plays one of the most furious games of tennis in California. His mathematical specialty is dynamic programming, which sets up a computer so that it can keep finding answers as the problem it is working on changes. Typical examples are the minute-to-minute guidance of a satellite or day-to-day analysis of the fluctuating stock market. The difficulty, says Dr. Bellman, is in formulating a problem. "We often find," he says, "that a good question is more important than a good answer."

THE "THREE-BODY" EXPERT

Examining a transparent celestial sphere is General Electric's cheerful specialist in space mechanics, Victor Szebehely *(left),* who enjoys predicting a phenomenon in the skies by deduction and letting someone else observe it in fact. "If he can't observe it," says Szebehely airily, "I don't admit that it doesn't exist. I say that he might not know how to observe." Recently he has been directing work on ways to slow down a spaceship before a moon landing. But he calls his most important contribution his study of the "three-body problem": calculating how three celestial bodies—the earth, the moon and a spaceship, for example—constantly change position in relation to one another. No one formula has yet been found to cover all celestial trios, but Szebehely's techniques have proved immensely valuable in space exploration.

Old-fashioned Mathematics and the H-bomb

From the inception of the atomic age, mathematicians have been as deeply involved in nuclear physics as physicists themselves. This remains true today, even though machines now do much work formerly done by human experts. The several hundred mathematicians recruited for the wartime Los Alamos project to develop the atomic bomb had at their disposal just one IBM machine, a rudimentary prototype of later computers. With a modern high-speed computer, their work could have been done in less than a hundredth of the time it actually took.

Yet in the postwar project to develop the H-bomb, Dr. Stanislaw Ulam (*right*) proved a match for the "thinking machines." A host of calculations had to be made to decide whether the bomb was feasible. The data were given to a team working with the computer ENIAC—and also to Dr. Ulam. Doing calculations the long, old-fashioned way, Ulam and one assistant turned in their answers even before the instructions to ENIAC had been completed. These figures disproved the first theories about the bomb, but Ulam came up with an approach that worked. His triumph over ENIAC led Dr. Edward Teller, head of the project, to remark later: "In a real emergency the mathematician still wins—if he is really good."

HIGH-SPEED CALCULATOR
Standing in front of an aluminum Cockcroft-Walton accelerator, a device which is used to study disintegrating protons at Los Alamos, is the brilliant theoretician Dr. Stanislaw Ulam. There is in the gentlest mathematician a hard quality of pride, and Dr. Ulam is no exception. He and the physicist Dr. Edward Teller joined forces in the development of the hydrogen bomb. When asked whether he worked with Teller, Ulam softly replied: "Dr. Teller worked with me."

3

An Alphabet
for Deciphering
the Unknown

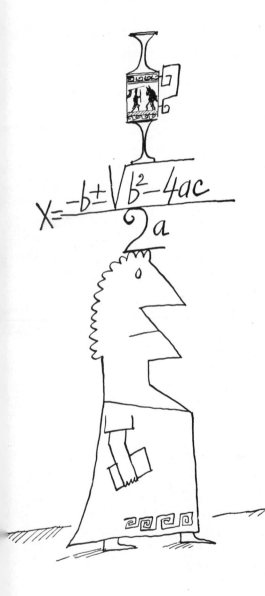

$$X = \frac{-b \pm \sqrt{b^2 - 4ac}}{2a}$$

A MATHEMATICAL CONFRONTATION
Saul Steinberg, the artist who often turns
mathematical symbols into humorous human
equations in *The New Yorker* magazine, here
represents the confrontation of the known and
the unknown as a solid businessman bearing a
number 5 meeting a lady wearing an algebraic
equation on her head. The headdress is the
solution of the so-called quadratic equation,
a useful tool in many basic algebra problems.

"AHA, ITS WHOLE, its seventh, it makes 19."

Strange-sounding patter this, suggestive of some occult ritual, but we echo it oftener than we realize. This brief sentence, discovered in a 3,600-year-old Egyptian papyrus, poses one of the first algebra problems known to have been solved by man. The explosive-sounding "Aha" is intended not as an exclamation but simply to designate "a heap," or "quantity." We use its equivalent every time we say: "Let x equal. . . ."

The papyrus of "Aha" came to the notice of Western scholars a century ago. Henry Rhind, a tuberculosis-ridden Scottish antiquary, bought it in 1858 in a shop in the Nile village of Luxor, where he was wintering for his health. Called the Rhind Papyrus in his honor, it is one of the earliest mathematical documents extant—an especially interesting one because of the evidence it contains that men in 1700 B.C. were already looking beyond arithmetic into the vistas of algebra. From the days of the pharaohs on down, the basic purpose of algebra has remained the same: to permit the solution of a mathematical problem which involves an unknown number. The unknown is expressed by an abstract symbol which is manipulated until its numerical value can be established. In order to pin the problem down and hold it securely while it is being turned around and simplified, the relationship between known and unknown numbers is set down in an equation—a statement of what equals what.

The venerable Egyptian problem of "Aha, its whole, its seventh, it makes 19" can readily be transmuted into 20th Century terms. A hard-pressed taxpayer faces the prospect of filing a declaration of estimated income tax. He knows that his actual tax will be $1,900. But he decides that if he slightly underestimates it at the beginning of the year—so that the balance he will have to make up at the end of the year does not exceed one seventh of what he has estimated—the Internal Revenue Service will not make a federal case out of it. Using the marvelously timesaving shorthand and rulebook logic of modern algebra, he says to himself: "Let x equal the number of hundreds of dollars I will declare as my tax. Then the problem is to find x so that x plus one seventh of it will equal 19." He expresses the entire problem as an equation. $x + x/7 = 19$ ("one seventh of x" being $x/7$). Then, almost automatically, he follows the axiom that equals multiplied by equals remain equal, and he multiplies both sides of the equation by 7 to arrive at a new equation, $7x + x = 133$. This in turn gives him $8x = 133$, then $x = 133/8$, and, finally, $x = 16\frac{5}{8}$, or, in another form, $16\frac{5}{8}$ hundreds of dollars—an estimated tax of $1,662.50. The ancient Egyptians also reached the answer of $16\frac{5}{8}$, although without the symbolic sort of equation we use today.

Many a citizen goes happily through life without ever needing to solve an algebraic equation from the time he leaves school. But in the vastly complicated world beyond his door, such equations are indispensable for reducing tough problems to simple terms. A corporation wrestles with an equation when it decides how long to keep a machine that depreciates at so many dollars per year before replacing it with a new piece of equipment that costs such-and-such. Algebra is used to determine how a timer should be set so that a bomb dropped from 10,000 feet, say, will explode 500 feet above the target. Few scientists can even talk without algebraic symbols to augment what they are saying. On office blackboards, cafeteria napkins or the hot sands of beaches, they are constantly scribbling equations—as terse summaries of past experiments or as handles with which to grasp at the possibilities of nature.

Modern algebra's procedures are as clear-cut as the regulations in an army manual. Write the problem as an equation in terms of x, the unknown number. Systematically arrange all the terms involving x on one side of the equation. Then combine and reduce them by symbolic arithmetic until a single x is left on one side and a known number on the other. This is the answer. Although simple-sounding in theory, in practice the transformations which have to be wrought to reduce the various terms involving x to a single x can be intricate and laborious. Sometimes it is helpful to break a problem down into several subproblems. Sometimes it is helpful to substitute for a combination of x's a single new unknown—a y or a z—which can be carried along like a traveler's check and then converted back into the hard cash of x at journey's end.

Algebra's major difficulties arise because some problems involve not just x, but also x^2 or x^3. The easy equations involving only x—and no higher power of x—are called first-degree, or linear, equations ("linear" meaning "one-dimensional"). Second-degree equations—containing no powers higher than x^2—are called quadratics (from "quadrate," or "squared number"). Equations of the third degree are called cubics; of the fourth degree, quartics. Beyond the quartics are indefinitely many equations of the fifth, sixth or umpteenth degree. Fortunately, these fearsome high-degree equations come up only occasionally.

The algebra of dinner for five

Most everyday problems in algebra—how fast to drive x miles to get to an appointment on time, how to convert a recipe for four into dinner for five—can be posed as linear equations. Quadratics come up mainly in two-dimensional problems, such as those involving area—how wide a sidewalk may be built around a rectangular lot of a certain size with a certain amount of cement. Cubics arise in three-dimensional problems, such as those concerning volume—how much metal is needed to build a million-gallon spherical oil tank. Quartics and higher-degree equations are required for complex scientific questions, such as finding the constant reproduction rate at which a bacterium will spawn a given num-

AN ANCIENT CALCULATION
This problem is from the Rhind Papyrus, among the earliest mathematical documents. Rendered here in hieroglyphics, it reads: "2/3 added and 1/3 taken away: 10 remains. Make 1/10 of this 10: the result is 1: remainder 9. Two thirds of it, namely 6, are added to it, total 15. A third of it is 5. It was 5 that was taken away: remainder 10." Translation: $x + 2/3x - 1/3(x + 2/3x) = 10$. In Egyptian symbolism, legs walking left mean "add"; walking right, "subtract."

ber of descendants in n generations—a so-called nth-degree equation. (Contrary to popular impression, the "nth degree" is not the "ultimate degree" to mathematicians but just any unspecified degree.)

To make matters easier all around, all equations of a given degree are viewed as a family. And just as each Scottish Highland clan has its own tartan, so each family of equations has its own representative "general equation." In this, a letter from the end of the alphabet—x, y or z—represents the unknown number, while letters from the beginning of the alphabet—a, b, c—represent numbers assumed to be known but not yet specified. Every quadratic equation, for instance, can be represented by the single general equation $ax^2 + bx + c = 0$. By solving this purely symbolic relationship, algebraists have found that the solution x is always

$$\frac{-b \pm \sqrt{b^2 - 4ac}}{2a}.$$

In this formula, familiar to all students of high-school algebra, the $\pm$ (plus-or-minus) sign means that there are two solutions to every quadratic equation—one which can be found by adding, the other by subtracting, at that particular point in the calculation.

Not surprisingly, the general solutions of the cubic and quartic families are correspondingly more complicated. As for the upper-crust equations beyond the quartic, no general solutions have been worked out at all. In fact, mathematicians have proved that equations beyond the fourth degree cannot be solved, by algebraic methods, in their full generality. With the help of the trial-and-error technique of an electronic computer, they can work out the solution for any specific problem involving a high-degree equation—but they cannot write down an exact algebraic formula for this solution.

Solving equations in algebra is greatly simplified by the signs and symbols that are employed; they serve as a shorthand to set in sharp relief both the problems and the logical steps for finding solutions. Astonishingly, in view of algebra's antiquity, the advantage of symbols went long unrealized. It was the 17th Century French philosopher-mathematician René Descartes who first used a, b and c to represent the known numbers and who, with a Gallic flair for the logical, decided that the other end of the alphabet should provide the symbols for the unknown. It was Descartes, too, who began to write x^2 in place of xx, or x^5 for $xxxxx$. From then on algebraic equations could be written in substantially their modern form.

Before an algebraic notation was developed, and before the birth of the idea that equations could be classified and that each class of equations had a general solution, algebra problems had the same dark fascination that riddles have. Each was a separate case with its own special solution. To the ancient mathematician, exploring his new-found land,

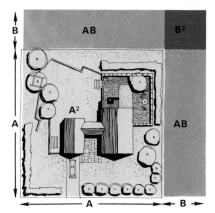

ALGEBRAIC EXPANSION
Suppose the plan for a new country cottage made the owner decide to enlarge his perfect square of land (whose side is a feet) by b feet on both north and east. How big would the new area $(a + b)^2$ be? If he constructed the above diagram he would see, by adding up the dimensions of all the small areas, that the answer is $a^2 + b^2 + 2ab$. Squaring $(a + b)$ was one of the early algebra problems worked out by the Greeks 2,000 years ago, using visual geometric methods much like this one.

each problem was an unexpected palace standing alone in a trackless wilderness. Today, looking at the terse records of early algebraic discoverers, we have no way of knowing what paths they took to their palaces and why. The first scholars who fully explained their methods for solving algebra problems—linear, quadratic and cubic—were the incomparable Greeks. But they wrote out their solutions in words and diagrams only—a long process and sometimes a confusing one.

Riddle in a life span

Then, in the twilight of the Greek era, a singular man appeared—Diophantus, who has been called the "Father of Algebra." Of his dates, we know only that they fell sometime between 100 and 400 A.D. By an odd happenstance, however, we do know precisely how long he lived—84 years. We have this information because one of his admirers described his life in terms of an algebraic riddle (shown below). Since the equation used to solve this riddle is an easy linear one, without any x^2 or x^3 in it, Diophantus himself would probably have turned up his nose at it. He was intent on tougher equations of other types.

Diophantus is remembered as the father of algebra because he was the first to abbreviate his thoughts systematically with symbols of his own devising and because he solved what are now called indeterminate, or "Diophantine," equations. Indeterminate equations do not contain enough information to be solved in specific numbers but enough to tie the answer down to a definite type. For instance: Mary is a year more than 10 times as old as Joan. What is Mary's age? Evidently, if Joan is 1, 2, 3, 4 . . . 100 . . . years old, Mary is 11, 21, 31, 41 . . . 1,001 . . . years old. The equation connecting their ages, $x = 10y + 1$, seems a trivial one at first sight, but it conjures up two entire parades of whole numbers marching in $x = 10y + 1$ step all the way to infinity. By using such infinite trains of numbers, correlated through Diophantine equations, modern mathematicians can study the properties of various types of whole numbers such as odds, evens, primes or squares, and can grasp some of the basic rules which numbers follow in playing the tricks they do.

The analysis of numbers that has grown from Diophantine equations is called the "theory of numbers" and is the purest of pure branches of present mathematics. Its development by Diophantus helped algebraists to look on an equation as a way of categorizing all numbers of a given type rather than as a relationship solely between the numbers of a specific problem. Algebra slowly began to unfold as a separate discipline.

During the Dark and Middle Ages a succession of Hindu and Moslem mathematicians handed algebra down from one oasis of culture—one sultanate or caliphate—to the next. They did not create much new knowledge in the process, but at least through practice they stripped the

$\frac{x}{6}$ The riddle begins: "Diophantus' youth lasted 1/6 of his life. [Letting x equal his life, his youth was therefore $x/6$.] $+\frac{x}{12}$ He grew a beard after 1/12 more. $+\frac{x}{7}$ After 1/7 more of his life, Diophantus married; five years . . . $+5$ . . . later he had a son.

art of equations of its aura of mystery. In 825 A.D. al-Khowarizmi, the same sage of Baghdad who had publicized the positional 10-system of writing numbers, wrote the first clear textbook on algebra. The title of this influential work was *al-jabr w'al-muqabalah*, which, translated from the Arabic, roughly means "the art of bringing together unknowns to match a known quantity." The key word in the title, *al-jabr*, or "bringing together," gave rise to our word algebra. Curiously, in medieval times "algebraist" could refer either to a man who brought bones together, i.e., a surgeon, or to a specialist in equations.

The most significant problem left hanging by al-Khowarizmi and his predecessors was how to interpret negative numbers—the numbers less than zero. After all, what could a negative number mean? Who ever held in his hand less than nothing? Today every beginning student in algebra learns by rote the so-called "law of signs"—that a plus times a plus equals a plus, that a minus times a minus equals a plus and that a plus times a minus equals a minus. The Hindus, it is believed, were among the first to perceive the possibilities of these combinations, and to realize that in solving a quadratic equation one can come up with a negative for an answer. Because 2×2 and -2×-2 both equal 4, for instance, the equation $x^2 = 4$ has not only the obvious solution $x = +2$ but also the solution $x = -2$.

The nonconformist negative

Since it is hard to grasp the idea of negative numbers, a long time elapsed before they were allowed into the parlors of mathematical propriety and common sense. One of the first to give them open-minded consideration was an Italian mathematician, Leonardo da Pisa, otherwise called "Fibonacci," who lived from about 1170 to 1250 A.D. On one occasion, while tackling a financial problem, he saw that it just could not be solved except in terms of a negative number. Instead of shrugging off this number, he looked it squarely in the eye and described it as a financial loss. "This problem," he wrote, "I have shown to be insoluble unless it is conceded that the first man had a debt."

Negative numbers can, of course, be interpreted in many other ways. They measure distances back along a road, temperatures below zero, times before the present or minutes before the hour. In general they are numbers with an arrow of direction built into them—an arrow that points backward from zero while the positive numbers point forward. As far as modern mathematicians are concerned, negative numbers need not be interpreted at all; they are simply useful abstractions.

Despite Fibonacci's tentative recognition that an equation might have a negative solution, most mathematicians continued to view negative numbers with cool disbelief until the 16th Century. In this, the era of

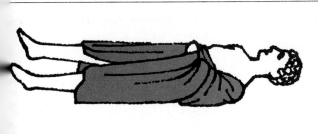

ALGEBRA SOLVES A RIDDLE
Little is known about the life of Diophantus, the Greek father of algebra, except his age at death, which has been preserved in the famous 1,500-year-old riddle shown here. Beginning at the far left of the opposite page, the riddle divides Diophantus' life into segments, each of which is a part of his total age (represented by x). The complete equation is:
$x = x/6 + x/12 + x/7 + 5 + x/2 + 4$, which reduces to $3x/28 = 9$, and finally, to 84 years.

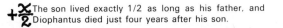

$+\dfrac{x}{2}$ The son lived exactly 1/2 as long as his father, and Diophantus died just four years after his son. $+4$ All of this adds up to the years Diophantus lived." $= x$

the Renaissance, when explorers in all fields were daily proving that they could go beyond the ancients and find new things under the sun, mathematics too enjoyed a new burst of creativity. Man's conception of numbers began to enlarge beyond the names and digits with which he could count pebbles on a beach. He began to see numbers as creations of his own mind; they were figments, perhaps, but figments which would some day enable him to envision atomic particles and to label points in space and time. This insight emerged in connection with the investigation of the cubic, or third-degree, equation, which happened to represent the outstanding mathematical problem of the time.

By the 16th Century, general solutions had been found for the linear and quadratic equations but not for the cubic—a rather infrequent equation involving x^3. But by 1550 the conquest of the cubic had been achieved by several independent approaches. And in applying these general formulas to particular equations, their discoverers could not help observing, with considerable unease, that the numbers involved in the procedure were not always the familiar positive ones.

Brainwork in a back alley

The men who bested the cubic, Italians all, were as colorful a crew of mathematicians as ever trod the boards of history. Most of them were self-made men, only a step removed from the countinghouse drudgery of solving compound-interest and simple insurance problems posed by the booming mercantile needs of the day. Having risen above mere practical reckoning, the great Italian algebraists were by and large a shrewd and opportunist lot, as much at home among the card cheats and stiletto-wielding assassins of Renaissance back alleys as they were in the university chairs to which they aspired and sometimes rose. To publicize their nimble-minded prowess they held problem-solving contests with one another, tests of strength on which their very livelihoods often depended. To make their sport doubly hazardous, they sometimes made up a purse and posted it with a third party—winner take all.

In this combative atmosphere, war broke out over the cubic equation. It may have been unwittingly sparked by a Franciscan friar, Luca Pacioli, who in 1494 published a compendium of algebra, the *Summa de Arithmetica.* In this work he relayed to less scholarly souls all the algebra invented to date, and closed with the nettling observation that mathematicians could not yet solve cubic equations by algebraic methods.

The first man to take up Pacioli's cubic challenge was Scipione del Ferro, a papermaker's son who had risen to become professor of mathematics at the University of Bologna. Finding the first general solution for all cubic equations of the simplified form $x^3 + ax = b$, del Ferro kept his discovery a secret, possibly to confound adversaries during compe-

AN EARLY "MAGIC" SQUARE
A favorite mathematical pastime is contriving "magic" squares. The square at right, created by the German painter Albrecht Dürer and incorporated into his famous engraving *Melancholia,* is arranged so that vertical, horizontal and diagonal rows add up to 34. The four middle boxes total 34. Dürer also managed to slip into the two center boxes at bottom the date of his square: 1514.

titions. But in his later years he confided his solution to his student Antonio Fior, who used it in an algebra match with a rival, Nicolo Fontana, called Tartaglia, or the "Stammerer," because as a boy he had had his palate cleft by a French saber.

By the time of the contest with Fior, Tartaglia had become one of the canniest equation-solvers in Italy and had devised a secret weapon of his own: a general solution for cubics of the type $x^3 + ax^2 = b$. As a result, when Fior tossed him a group of specific examples of the $x^3 + ax = b$ type, he countered with examples of the $x^3 + ax^2 = b$ type. During the interval allowed for working out the answers, both Tartaglia and Fior worked feverishly, but when time was up and the day of reckoning had arrived, Tartaglia had solved all Fior's problems and Fior had solved none of Tartaglia's. The Stammerer's genius had responded to pressure by conceiving a general solution for *both* types of cubic equations.

As a new ranking calculator of Italy, Tartaglia soon came up against a stiffer antagonist—Girolamo Cardano. The illegitimate son of a lawyer and himself the father of a murderer, Cardano was an astrologer who cast horoscopes for kings, a physician who attended their sickbeds and a scientific writer from whose quill books flowed in fountains. He was also a compulsive gambler, forever teetering on the verge of bankruptcy and prison—when not on the brink of atheism and heresy. But Cardano always landed on his feet. The Pope gave him a pension and Tartaglia gave him his solution to the cubic equation. Cardano got it by brandishing shrewder flattery than the Stammerer knew how to parry.

Though Cardano swore to keep Tartaglia's cubic solution secret, he published it a few years later, in 1545, in a monumental treatise on equations, his *Ars Magna (Great Art)*. Tartaglia, who had been about to write his own book, spent the rest of his life railing against Cardano for sharp practice. Yet Cardano's book gave Tartaglia full credit for his discovery. It also enshrined in history the brawling, blasphemous Lodovico Ferrari, who died at the age of 43, poisoned, it is believed, by his own sister. As Tartaglia had solved the cubic, so Ferrari, when still a student—Cardano's—had solved the fourth-degree, or quartic, equation. By disclosing the work of both men, Cardano in his *Ars Magna* was able to give the world the general solutions to cubics and quartics at once—to announce the first two significant algebraic advances since the death of Diophantus some 1,300 years earlier.

In the *Ars Magna* Cardano formally accepted the concept of negative numbers and enunciated the laws which govern them. He also advanced yet another kind of new number which he called a "fictitious" or "sophistic" quantity. This was the square root of a negative number and even harder to grasp than a negative number itself, since no real number multiplied by itself can produce a negative number. Today mathemati-

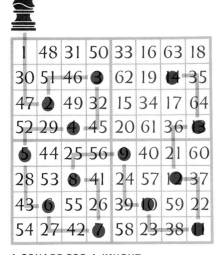

A SQUARE FOR A KNIGHT
The 18th Century mathematician Leonhard Euler made a square *(above)* where each horizontal or vertical row totals 260; stopping halfway on each gives 130. Even more intriguing is that a chess knight, starting its L-shaped moves (brown lines) from box 1, can hit all 64 boxes in numerical order.

52	61	4	13	20	29	36	45
14	3	62	51	46	35	30	19
53	60	5	12	21	28	37	44
11	6	59	54	43	38	27	22
55	58	7	10	23	26	39	42
9	8	57	56	41	40	25	24
50	63	2	15	18	31	34	47
16	1	64	49	48	33	32	17

A WELL-ROUNDED SQUARE
Benjamin Franklin created a magic square full of tricks *(above)*. Each row adds up to 260; stopping halfway on each makes 130. Tracing a dotted diagonal up four boxes and down four boxes makes 260. The four corners plus the four middle numbers are 260. The sum of the numbers in any four-box subsquare is 130 —as is the sum of any four numbers that lie equidistant from the square's center.

cians call the square root of a negative number, such as $\sqrt{-2}$, an "imaginary" number. When such a quantity is combined with a real number, such as in $1+\sqrt{-2}$, the result is known as a "complex" number.

Later mathematicians have shown that complex numbers can have all sorts of applications: they provide solutions to equations concerning, for instance, the "states" of atomic particles in atomic physics. Like many concepts of mathematics, they are best accepted as pure abstractions. Cardano's premonition as to their importance, however, was more than justified when the 19th Century mathematical genius Carl Friedrich Gauss proved that every equation has exactly as many positive, negative or complex solutions as the degree of the equation itself. Every first-degree equation has one solution, every second-degree equation has two solutions, every third-degree equation has three solutions, every nth-degree equation has n solutions. This satisfying symmetry is called the "fundamental theorem of algebra."

Largely because of Cardano, mathematics returned from its fling in the bordellos of the Renaissance enormously enriched. The Italians had shown that new breakthroughs could be made beyond the knowledge of ancient times. Strict deduction and proof, after the Greek pattern, did not always need to precede discovery. European mathematicians had revived the freewheeling spirit of Archimedes.

The Magnificent Heritage of Ancient Cultures

Mathematics had its crude beginnings perhaps 50 centuries ago in the civilizations of the Middle East. For the Babylonians and the Egyptians it was a practical tool, essential in day-to-day living. Astronomers reckoned the movements of sun and moon so they could mark the seasons and keep track of harvests and festivals. Men learned to measure and count so they might tally their flocks and trade their produce. With geometry the volume of a cylindrical granary could be calculated; with advanced arithmetic the value of its grain content could be measured. In Egypt, Herodotus wrote, land was divided by "assigning square plots of ground of equal size to all," for which all paid rent. If a man's land was flooded, his loss was measured and he paid rent "proportionate to the reduced size of his land." Soon the men of this region were venturing into mathematics of increasing complexity. And in the art and tools of each period, as in the Persian miniature opposite, they left behind a fascinating record of their mathematical progress.

MATHEMATICIANS OF ISLAM
In seeking to chart the courses of the stars, the astronomers of medieval Islam made use of the most comprehensive mathematics the world had known to that time. This 16th Century Persian illumination shows a group of turbaned astronomers working in their observatory with an array of instruments including compasses, a globe of the world, astrolabes and a mechanical clock.

EARLY CHRISTIAN STARGAZERS
This 13th Century French miniature, the frontispiece to a psalm book, shows three medieval monks practicing astronomical techniques newly introduced from Islam. The man in the center sights a star along the bar of an astrolabe as an assistant at the right reads from astronomical tables, and a clerk *(left)* records the observations. They may have been working on a calendar.

The Pervasive Influence of the Stars

From the earliest times, mathematicians have fastened their gaze on the heavens. Islamic astronomers of the Middle Ages—having learned from captured Greek texts how to build mathematical instruments—were setting up observatories and charting the movements of stars and planets while contemporary Europeans were ignorant of nearly all ancient science.

However, as mathematical knowledge filtered into a Renaissance Europe in love with science but still married to superstition, a sharp division began to appear between the true science of astronomy and the pseudo science of astrology. "God did not create the planets and stars with the intention that they should dominate man," the great Swiss physician Paracelsus commented in 1541, "but that they, like other creatures, should obey and serve him."

MOSLEM MAP OF THE HEAVENS
This 13th Century astrolabe is engraved with a star map which can be rotated to find the position of stars on any night. On its opposite side is a movable bar used for sighting the angle that sun and stars make with the horizon, in order to determine latitude and the time of day.

ASTROLOGY WITHOUT STARS
Using a geomantic calculator like the one above, 13th Century Moslems could cast a horoscope based on chance rather than observation. Lots were drawn and the results, registered on the calculator dial, gave the planets arbitrary positions from which the horoscope could be cast.

FIGURING THE EARTH'S TILT
By aligning the top rings of an armillary sphere *(left)* with various celestial bodies, Moslem astronomers of the 16th Century could calculate the time of day or year, or measure the tilt of the earth's axis or the height of the sun. This instrument is an exact copy of an ancient Greek model.

A Mathematics for Farmers, Surveyors and Pyramid Builders

ENGINEERING FOR THE DEAD
This plummet, used by Egyptian builders to find the vertical in cutting and fitting bricks or stones, was also an amulet placed in tombs for good luck in afterlife. With such tools they performed engineering marvels. The stones of the Great Pyramid have a mean variation from a straight line of only 1/100 of an inch, and they were brought as close together as 1/500 of an inch.

Few of the ancients left a more impressive record of practical achievements than did the Egyptians. Their massive pyramids were great engineering achievements and also masterpieces of mathematical sophistication. Using instruments like the one at left, Egyptian builders made the four sides of the Great Pyramid of Cheops face directly north, south, east and west, accurate to an astounding 1/12 of a degree. Within the pyramids and other tombs is more evidence of the Egyptians' mathematical prowess. Murals like those shown

here demonstrate the many ways in which mathematics was put to work—counting geese, dividing the harvests, surveying the fields after the Nile floods receded.

The Egyptians were strongest in geometry. They had rough formulas for finding the volume of solids, like a pile of grain and the baskets for carrying it (*mural above*). And although compared to the Olympian grandeur of Greek geometry Egyptian mathematics was little more than a tool, it was a tool made razor-sharp by the constant honing of everyday use.

KEEPING ACCOUNT OF DAILY LIFE
The above reproduction of a 3,000-year-old mural shows (top level) surveyors carrying a knotted cord. A rope of this sort, with 12 equidistant knots pulled into a triangle with sides of three, four and five units, gives a right-angled triangle, which the Egyptians may have used in fixing land boundaries. The lower level of the mural shows baskets of grain being brought to a storehouse as scribes keep the accounts.

A HIGH CASTE OF ACCOUNTANTS
The Egyptians considered mathematics so important that its mysteries were entrusted to a privileged hereditary class of scribes, who kept all accounts, public and private. The fragment of a mural at left depicts a scribe at his desk. The lower section shows the scribe unrolling a new papyrus with his back to bowing gooseherds, one of whom fills his baskets with geese.

Among the Ancients, an Accurate Count of the Hours and Days

Civilization and schedules go hand in hand—and schedules mean timekeeping, and thus mathematics. From the beginning, time was linked with the movements of celestial bodies. Computing the length of a day from the earth's rotation was simple; figuring the number of days in a year from the earth's revolution around the sun was more complicated. Yet as early as 3000 B.C. the Babylonians had divided the year into 360 days—a relatively advanced mathematical feat. Egyptian calendars were even more accurate, with a 365-day year and—later—provision for a quadrennial leap year. Until modern times, calendars were owned only by the church and the nobility; many of them were elaborate and beautifully decorated, like the Book of Hours at right.

No one knows when man first discovered that a stick's shadow could measure the sun's movements across the sky, but it was certainly before 1500 B.C., the date of the oldest known sundial. After the sundial came water clocks, sandglasses and burning cándles. But the need for a shady-day timekeeper that did not require constant attention was not satisfied until about the 14th Century, with the invention of the mechanical clock. Like calendars, the first timepieces belonged only to the few. The poor measured their time by counting the tolling of church bells, about the only mathematics they knew.

GRAVITY KEEPS THE HOURS
Spectators look with amazement at the strange mechanical clock depicted in this 15th Century French miniature. Invention of such instruments was a feat of technology based on a solid mathematical foundation. Most medieval mechanical timepieces like this got their power from a suspended weight whose gradual descent turned a series of wheels geared to drive its single hand.

A SUNDIAL FOR THE POCKET
The portable 15th Century sundial at left came complete with a compass under the lid in the center. More complex dials reveal how technology was maturing in the late Middle Ages; their accessories included an adjustment for different latitudes and a plummet for leveling.

A GOLDEN BOOK OF HOURS
This painting embellished with gold is from the world's most magnificent calendar, the 15th Century Duc de Berry's Book of Hours. The mathematical influence of the Moslems was widely apparent in Europe, as shown by the Hindu-Arabic numerals for the 30 days of November (inside ring of semicircle). The next three rings forecast new moons for a 19-year period. Three outside rings show astrological signs for November.

77

After a Dark Age, the Flowering of the Science of Numbers

By the time of the Greeks, mathematics had become such a vast body of knowledge that it could no longer be passed along by word of mouth. The Greeks wrote hundreds of books on the subject, treating it for the first time as a matter worthy of study on its own, not just as a useful tool. In the centuries of darkness that followed, much of this mathematical treasury was lost. But enough remained so that the scholars of the late Middle Ages, once again launched on a search for knowledge, unearthed the ancient classics and translated them into many languages, giving the study of mathematics an impetus that has been accelerating for the last 500 years.

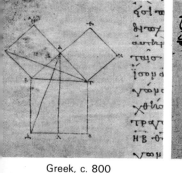

Greek, c. 800

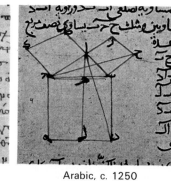

Arabic, c. 1250

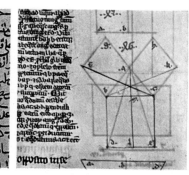

Latin, 1120

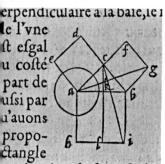

French, 1564

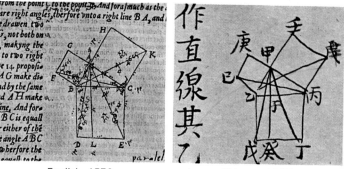

English, 1570

Chinese, 1607

A GLOBE-GIRDLING THEOREM
The Pythagorean theorem, first expounded more than 2,000 years ago, was familiar all over the civilized world by the 17th Century. At top left is a Greek text of Euclid's proof, and with it five translations. Although the Chinese text is only 350 years old, the Chinese were actually familiar with the theorem at about the time of Pythagoras.

EDUCATION-STARVED EUROPEANS
This 16th Century French tapestry shows "Madame Arithmetic" teaching young noblemen to calculate, using table-top counters manipulated like abacus beads. By this time European youths, emerging from the ignorance of medievalism, were flocking to new schools for education. One of the standard subjects was arithmetic.

Arismetique

4

A Happy Marriage of Curves and Quantities

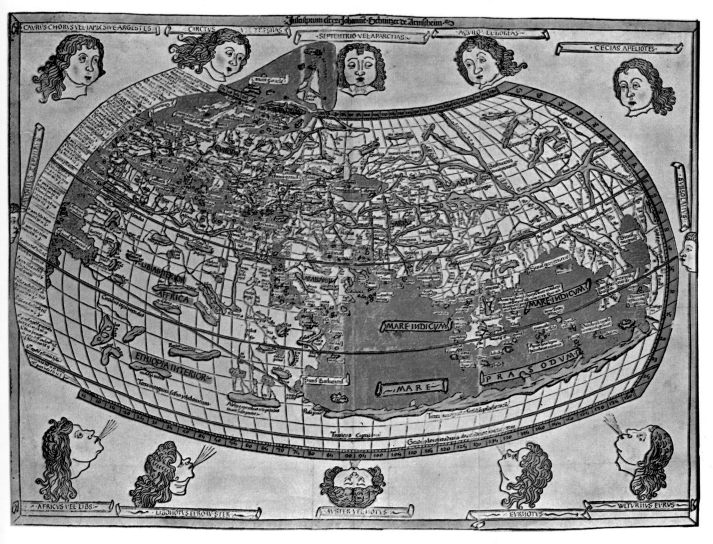

STAKING OUT THE EARTH
The 15th Century German map above, drawn
on principles laid down by Ptolemy in 150 A.D.,
is one of the first known maps to use curved
lines of latitude and longitude to pinpoint
locations on earth. In analytic geometry,
developed in the 17th Century, similar "grids"
are used to locate points on a plane surface.

IN 1616 a young French aristocrat named René Descartes graduated in law from the University of Poitiers and set out to remake the world. He was deeply dissatisfied with what he had learned of it from academicians still in thrall to the thinkers of antiquity. Descartes disdained the philosophy of the ancients as distinctly short of the mark. "I saw," he later recalled, "that it had been cultivated for many ages by the most distinguished men, and that yet there is not a single matter within its sphere which is not still in dispute."

Descartes felt confident that he could remedy all this bungling. Although a not uncommon ambition in a 20-year-old, in his case it was to have a most uncommon outcome. He was to do all that he dreamed, and to recast human thought as only a handful of men have done in the course of history. What is still more unusual, he was to work his revolution with a fresh philosophy that grew out of mathematics. And in the process he was to develop his own new branch of mathematics. This was "analytic geometry," which merged all the arithmetic, algebra and geometry of ages past in a single technique—a technique of visualizing numbers as points on a graph, equations as geometric shapes, and shapes as equations. By unifying elementary mathematics, analytic geometry became the bedrock on which was built most of today's higher mathematics and much of the exact sciences.

The world into which Descartes sallied in the winter of 1616 was alive with fresh ideas and bold deeds: Protestants proclaiming their stern standards of individual conscience; cavaliers defending their prickly prides with quick swords; rival nations scheming for overseas empires; Dutch fur traders making deals in Manhattan; English settlers struggling for survival at Jamestown. London theatergoers were mourning the recent death of Shakespeare. Monteverdi was composing the world's first grand operas. William Harvey had just begun the lectures in which he described the heart not as a seat of emotion but as a pump for the blood. Kepler was preparing to publish the third and last of his laws which describe exactly how the planets orbit around the sun. The idea that the sun is the center of the solar system—propounded by the Polish astronomer-monk Copernicus—had just been branded as heresy by the Holy Office in Rome; Galileo, busy with his newfangled telescope, had been warned to give up his enthusiastic support of the notion.

Riding the wide wave of creativity, young Descartes came to the conviction that the world needed a formula which would discipline rational thought and unify knowledge. Having turned his back on the philosophy of the past, he set out to find such a formula in "knowledge of myself" and in the "great book of the world." After a brief probe into the pleasures of Paris, he turned gentleman-soldier, first for the Dutch Prince of Nassau, then for the German Duke of Bavaria. While soldiering he spent

THE HOUSE ON THE CORNER
This map demonstrates how the intersection of two streets can locate a dwelling. Without chance of confusion, the owner could direct visitors to his home by saying simply that he lived at the corner of Second Avenue and Third Street.

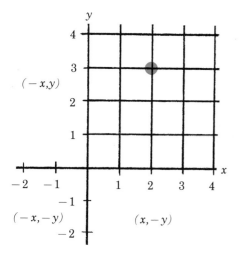

GETTING TO THE POINT
A grid of lines similar to the street arrangement above locates points on a surface. Mathematicians say the point shown here is at 2, 3. The first number is the distance along the horizontal, or *x*, axis and the second the distance along the vertical, or *y*, axis.

most of his time, as he himself put it, "over Head and Ears in the Study of mathematics," the one branch of learning which "delighted . . . on account of the certitude of its proofs and evidence of its reasonings." Within two years, at the age of 22, he began to develop his "analytic geometry." Within another year he had also glimpsed "the method of right reasoning" which was to make him famous as a philosopher.

A session in a stove

This "method," although it had long been germinating, flashed into his conscious mind during a single day of revelation in an army camp on the banks of the Danube. It was a cold day and Descartes spent it meditating in a small, heated room known in those times as a "stove." What he formulated in the stove, and subsequently elaborated, was the doctrine that all knowledge—both past and future—should be worked out in terms of mathematical reasoning. Descartes proposed that contemporary scholars cease to rely so heavily upon ancient ideas and make a fresh start. He urged that they try to explain all nature by a deductive scheme of science. This, he felt, should begin with the simplest axiomatic verities and proceed—with a modicum of help from experiments—to the most complex understandings. "The long chains of simple and easy reasonings by means of which geometers are accustomed to reach the conclusions of their most difficult demonstrations," he wrote, "had led me to imagine that all things to the knowledge of which men are competent are mutually connected in the same way."

This vision of Descartes has inspired man ever since and, indeed, remains the ambition of all modern science. But Descartes himself had great difficulty in establishing the basic axioms from which his grand design was to grow. The more he looked for fundamental truths, the fewer he could find. In the end he could find none except the simple assertion, *Cogito, ergo sum*—"I think, therefore I am"—by which he meant that he could find no better basis from which to start understanding the real world of tables and chairs than man's ability to use his own mind.

Not until 18 years after his revelation in the stove did Descartes share his philosophy with the public. He made an interim attempt at a book and then voluntarily suppressed it, in deference to his Catholic faith, because it subscribed to the heretical ideas of Copernicus about the universe. Finally, after repeated urgings by friends, Descartes in 1637 published *Discourse on the Method of Rightly Conducting the Reason.* Still regarded as a major work of philosophy, it immediately stamped him as one of the great thinkers of his age.

Descartes concluded *The Method* with three concrete examples of how it might be applied. The first two sought to explain the behavior of lenses and of shooting stars. The third was a 106-page footnote, *The Geometry,* which mathematicians still affectionately refer to by its original French title of *La Géométrie*. This lengthy appendage, which outlined analytic geometry, constituted, in the words of the 19th Century British philosopher John Stuart Mill, "the greatest single step ever made in the progress of the exact sciences." It is strange that Descartes buried this jewel at the end of his book. In the next three centuries analytic geometry was to outstrip philosophy in creating the science Descartes dreamed of. And yet he himself never pursued it beyond his original summary.

La Géométrie set forth the idea that a pair of numbers can determine a position on a surface: one number as a distance measured horizontally, the other as a distance measured vertically. This idea, of course, has since become familiar to anyone who has used graph paper, read a street map, or studied latitude and longitude lines in an atlas. Graph paper had not yet been invented in Descartes' day, but the concept of the graph itself, with its use of crossed lines for reference purposes, was contained in his work. Descartes showed that with a pair of intersecting straight lines as yardsticks, a whole network of reference lines could be constructed on which numbers could be designated as points; that if algebraic equations were represented as sequences of points, they would appear as geometric shapes; and that geometric shapes, in turn, could be translated into sequences of numbers represented as equations. In Descartes' honor we call the original intersecting straight lines the system of "Cartesian coordinates," with the vertical line known as the y axis, the horizontal line as the x axis. How the Cartesian graph works in terms of a street map is seen on the opposite page.

In the concept of coordinates with which he launched his analytic geometry, Descartes gave all mathematicians of then and thereafter a stimulating new way to look at mathematical information. He showed, for instance, that all second-power, or quadratic, equations, when graphed as connected points, become straight lines, circles, ellipses, parabolas or hyperbolas—the conic sections on which Apollonius had lavished so much ingenuity 1,900 years earlier. The equation $x^2 - y^2 = 0$, when graphed, becomes two straight crossed lines, the equation $x^2 + y^2 = 4$ becomes a circle, $x^2 - y^2 = 4$ a hyperbola, $x^2 + 2y^2 = 4$ an ellipse, and $x^2 = 4y$ a parabola (illustrated at right). What is more, Descartes went on to show that the general equation representing all quadratics, $ax^2 + bxy + cy^2 = d$, inevitably turns into a conic curve when graphed.

Going beyond the quadratic to cubics, quartics and equations of even higher degree, Descartes established that each class of equations brings into being a whole new tribe of curves—hearts, hummocks, petal shapes, loops, figure eights. The degree of an equation determines the maximum number of intersection points that the curve of the equation can have

DRAWING AN EQUATION
The drawings at right show some familiar geometric shapes with equations that produce them. To make the graph of an equation: let x equal a number; solve the equation for y; put a point on the paper located by these values of x and y as explained in the bottom drawing on the opposite page. Let x equal another number, find y and put that point on the page. The line connecting many such points is the graph of the equation.

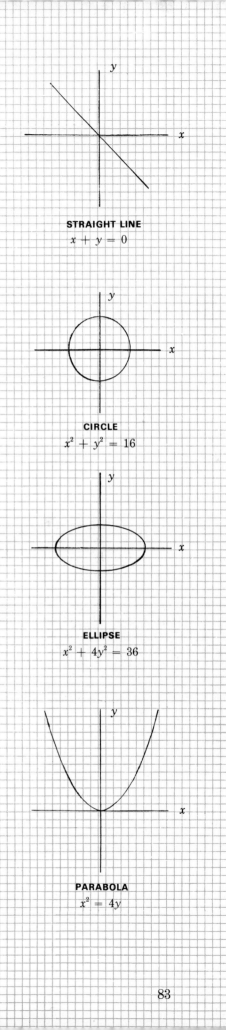

STRAIGHT LINE
$x + y = 0$

CIRCLE
$x^2 + y^2 = 16$

ELLIPSE
$x^2 + 4y^2 = 36$

PARABOLA
$x^2 = 4y$

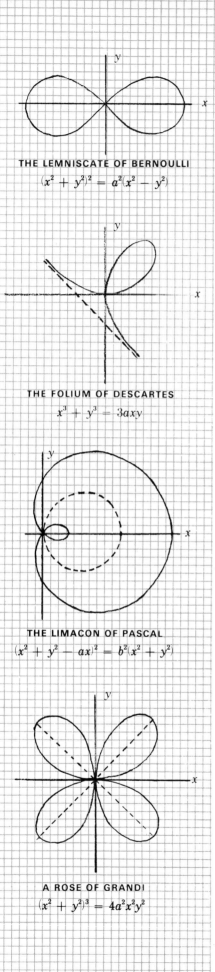

THE LEMNISCATE OF BERNOULLI
$$(x^2 + y^2)^2 = a^2(x^2 - y^2)$$

THE FOLIUM OF DESCARTES
$$x^3 + y^3 = 3axy$$

THE LIMACON OF PASCAL
$$(x^2 + y^2 - ax)^2 = b^2(x^2 + y^2)$$

A ROSE OF GRANDI
$$(x^2 + y^2)^3 = 4a^2x^2y^2$$

with a straight line. A first-degree curve—that is, a straight line—can intersect another straight line only once. A second-degree conic curve can be cut by a straight line at only two points. Cubic curves, which a straight line can intersect three times, are often S-shaped. Fourth-degree curves, with four possible intersection points, may have the shape of a W or a figure 8. The hourglass of the feminine figure, it may be noted in passing, translates algebraically into the specific quartic equation $(x^2 + y^2 + a^2)^2 - 4a^2y^2 = c^4$.

The curves which represent any one degree of equation have many other traits in common—so many, in fact, that each is a class unto itself, and a mathematician can say "fifth-degree" or "seventh-degree" curve to a colleague and conjure up a large array of specific geometric features peculiar to all members of the particular curvaceous tribe in question.

Thanks to analytic geometry, every equation can be converted into a geometric shape and every geometric shape into an equation. Some shapes, to be sure, can be represented only by indefinitely long equations and some equations represent shapes hard to visualize—full of dips and doubling-backs. But every shape has its equivalent in algebraic form.

In its all-encompassing embrace of past mathematical knowledge, analytic geometry was to grow far beyond Descartes' original brief presentation, and was to touch nothing in mathematics without transforming it. Branches of mathematical thought which had seemed sidelines were now brought into the mainstream. One was the ancient technique of trigonometry; another was the fledgling device of logarithms.

Removing the pi in the sky

Trigonometry—the study of triangles—had served, from early Babylon until just prior to Descartes, as a purely practical adjunct of surveying, astronomy and navigation. Stargazers and sailors alike, scanning the heavens or the seas, often needed to calculate distances immeasurable by ruler or tape. Trigonometry permitted them to do so by simply applying certain basic rules about the relationships between the sides and angles of any triangle, however large or small. These relationships, or ratios, were initially established by the Greeks to analyze the arcs of circles. The first man known to have employed such relationships was the astronomer Hipparchus, who used them around 140 B.C. to find straight-line distances across the curved vault of the heavens—an attempt, as it were, to eliminate the pi in the sky. Today the three most-used ratios concern the right triangle, and are called the sine (sin for short), the cosine (cos) and the tangent (tan). Precisely what these ratios represent, and how the homeowner applies them to fell a tree outside his house without smashing the roof, may be seen on page 86.

The ratios represented by the sine, cosine and tangent of an angle

CURVES WITH A VERVE
These fancy curves with fancy names are examples of mathematical showmanship by mathematicians Bernoulli, Descartes, Étienne Pascal and Grandi, and they have little practical value. Yet each of the curves is an actual graph of the equation below it and is traced in precisely the same way as the simpler figures on the previous page, by letting x in the equation take on a series of different values.

change in numerical value as the angle changes in size. The Greeks calculated some of these values and arranged them in trigonometric tables which later mathematicians improved and extended. These tables remained, for a long time, merely a form of applied mathematics —the tool of celestial and earthly navigators. Then the remarkable French algebraist Francis Vieta, who preceded Descartes by half a century, made a vital observation. He perceived that a trigonometric ratio could be used to solve an algebraic equation; that, in effect, a series of numbers in a table could represent the successive values taken on by an unknown. The statement that "the sine of angle x is y" can also be put as "$y = \sin x$," an equation every bit as valid, say, as $y = x^2 + 7x$. The way Vieta's insight broadened the scope of trigonometry became even clearer when Descartes came along with his graphing technique. An equation like $y = \sin x$ could now be actually graphed, point by point, to create a curve on paper; it is, incidentally, an endless wavy line—the exact graphic equivalent of the pulsating ebb and flow of electric current in an ordinary A.C. power cable.

As it did with trigonometry, the Cartesian system reached out and took in the sideline of mathematics known to every teenager as "logarithms." Like trigonometry, logarithms involve relationships between numbers. A logarithm is the "exponent" of a number, indicating to what power the number must be raised in order to produce another given number. By familiarizing himself with logarithms, anyone confronted with arduous multiplications and divisions can save himself a lot of sheer arithmetic drudgery. This was precisely the intent of the inventor of logarithms, John Napier, Baron of Merchiston, the same man who first used the decimal point in its modern context.

This modest Scotsman conceived the idea of logarithms four decades before Descartes published his *Method*. The essence of Napier's discovery, as developed by later mathematicians, is that any number, of any size, can be expressed in terms of the power to which another number, the "base," must be raised to give the original number. For example, 100 is 10^2, 56 is $10^{1.74819}$ and 23 is $10^{1.36173}$. Further, when exponents of these last two 10s are added together, the result is a new power of 10, $10^{3.10992}$, which, when worked out, is 1,288, or 56 multiplied by 23. Subtracting the smaller of these same two exponents from the larger yields $10^{.38646}$, which, when worked out, is the number that results from dividing 56 by 23, 2.4348. Mathematicians have enunciated all this in the so-called "laws of exponents": adding exponents is equivalent to multiplication, and subtracting them is equivalent to division.

Napier arranged his logarithmic calculations in convenient tables which are used daily by scientists and engineers enmeshed in multidigit calculations. To figure out 56 times 23, of course, should require no more

A MISLABELED HONOR
In 1937, France issued a postage stamp honoring René Descartes on the 300th anniversary of his invention of analytic geometry. The first issue *(above)* incorrectly titled Descartes' masterwork *Discours sur la méthode,* which had to be changed in a second issue to its accurate title of *Discours de la méthode (below).* So many erroneous stamps were printed that their value to collectors is no more than that of the corrected version.

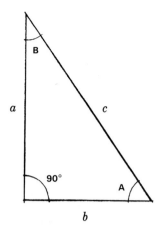

MEASURING THE TRIANGLE
The table below shows that the sine, cosine and tangent of the small angles of a right triangle are ratios between the triangle's sides. Therefore, knowing two sides, or one side and one angle, it is possible to find all the sides and angles of the triangle.

$$\text{Sine angle } A = \frac{a}{c} \qquad \text{Sine angle } B = \frac{b}{c}$$

$$\text{Cosine angle } A = \frac{b}{c} \qquad \text{Cosine angle } B = \frac{a}{c}$$

$$\text{Tangent angle } A = \frac{a}{b} \qquad \text{Tangent angle } B = \frac{b}{a}$$

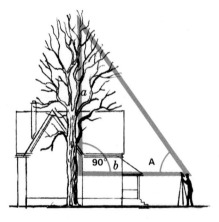

A USEFUL TANGENT
Measuring a tree uses the tangent formula above. Find angle *A* with a transit and distance b with a tape. The tangent of *A* (found in a trigonometric table) equals *a* divided by *b*. Solving this equation gives the height of the tree above the transit.

than pencil and scratch paper or, at most, the handy aid to short calculation known as a slide rule—a gadget consisting of a pair of rulers marked off in logarithmic scales and fastened together so they can slide on one another (illustrated below). Where Napier's noble handiwork shows up best is in the wearisome longer computations—when, for instance, an economist decides to divide $503,443,000,000, our gross national product for 1960, by our population for that year, 179,323,175.

The development of the Cartesian system made it possible to draw curves for logarithmic relationships like $y = \log x$ as easily as it did for trigonometric ratios like $y = \sin x$. By permitting such equations, as well as all algebraic equations, to be displayed in visible, viable lines and points, the Cartesian graph in effect captured and tamed the changing relationships between interconnected quantities. Out of this triumph emerged a concept fundamental to all higher mathematics: the idea of "variables" and "functions."

If an x and a y can be related through an equation or graph, they are called "variables": that is, one changes in value as the other changes in value. The two have what is known as a functional relationship; the variable whose change of value comes about as a result of the other variable's change of value is called a "function" of that other variable. A sine or a cosine or a tangent of an angle is a function of that angle; likewise, a logarithm is a function of the number it represents. In an ordinary algebraic equation, y is a function of x if y's value changes when the value of x changes.

Although seemingly of remote concern to anyone but the mathematician, the idea of variables and functions has come to be ubiquitous. If the humidity in the air is shown to be affected by the temperature, it is a function of temperature. An executive's blood pressure, rising with each birthday, is a function of his age. The ground covered by his car is a function of the time he takes and of the speed at which he drives.

Beyond giving impetus to the concept of variables and functions, beyond providing fuller scope for earlier mathematical discoveries, the Cartesian system's basic contribution to mathematics was essentially a philosophical one. By allowing a broad interchangeability of viewpoints, it gave rise to the mathematical freedom now known as "analysis," which encompasses most of the higher mathematics invented since Descartes' day. An algebraist who embarks on one of his more abstract outings and becomes doubtful about his direction can draw curves for his equations, thereby making the xs and ys come clearer. The practitioner of geometry, on the other hand, can perform long chains of reasoning with lightning speed simply by manipulating shapes as equations.

In all manner of concrete applications, every change and movement in nature can now be considered in the double-barreled form of equation-

or-curve. A bridge builder can write the curve of a slack cable as an equation and, through its xs and ys, gain more understanding of the stresses on the bridge. Most important of all, the experimental scientist, using graphs, can convert all the interrelationships and fluctuations which he measures in nature into sets of numbers which can be plotted on paper. If, after repeated trial of a single experiment, he obtains the same curve and equation, he may arrive at a law which is worth interpreting in words and ideas. Once fully understood, it may be combined with other formulas—other laws written as equations—to suggest new possibilities about nature and new experiments.

Philosophy in a plumed hat

The man who opened the gateway to higher mathematics did not, ironically enough, dally long with mathematics himself. Instead Descartes turned professionally to philosophy, resolved to re-create it according to his own lights. Back in Paris from the wars, he cut a colorful, eccentric figure—with a sword at his belt, a plumed hat and an intriguing line of talk about the changes which his new mathematical philosophy would bring about in the world. Having invested his inheritance shrewdly, he lived in complete leisure, enjoying ill-health and never rising before 11 a.m. Admirers plagued him; he was eternally seeking peace and quiet in which to think, eternally fleeing from one rented château to another. He dabbled about with investigations into human physiology, animal cadavers, glaciers, meteors, rainbows and mountain heights. Well before the actual publication of his *Method*, he hinted that he had found a means of making man omniscient.

When Paris palled, Descartes moved to Holland. Here, in 1637, his monumental work finally saw the light of print. During his long procrastination over its publication, another mathematician, the number theorist Pierre de Fermat, had independently developed a goodly part of analytic geometry on his own. But Fermat, too, was slow about writing up his ideas and so, in the end, Descartes was not robbed of the credit for his invention. Seemingly indifferent to its reception, he spent most of his time in a strange, compulsive round of new châteaux and new seclusions. Only the French friar Father Mersenne, who served as the scientific clearinghouse of the age and transmitted all Descartes' communications to fellow philosophers and mathematicians, ever knew his address at any one moment.

Descartes came to an end as appalling in its seriocomic way as the tragic deaths of Archimedes and Hypatia. During his Dutch sojourn, his fame somehow reached the ear of Queen Christina of Sweden, a 19-year-old girl of tremendous ability, indomitable will and almost superhuman stamina. As a horsewoman, she could stay in the saddle for 10 hours and

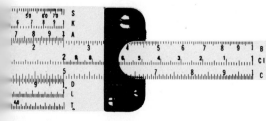

"SLIP-STICK" COMPUTING
Slide rules are, in effect, compact logarithm tables that make speedy calculation possible. In this example, multiplying 2 by 3, the index (1) of the C scale is placed over the 2 on the D scale below. The hairline on the slide is put over the 3 on the C scale. The answer, 6, appears where the hairline crosses the D scale. To multiply 3 by 4, the 1 of the C scale would be placed over the 3 on the D scale and the hairline over the 4 of the C scale, etc.

never notice the feelings or fallings of the intellectual men she delighted in and kept in her retinue.

Descartes rebuffed this amazon of the North for a whole year, but when she sent a battleship for him, the flattery was too much for him and he marched bravely aboard. Christina had great hopes for him. He was to help her found a Swedish academy of arts and letters and he was to instruct her privately in philosophy during the devotional hour of 5 to 6 a.m., when her day began. Liberally she gave him a three-week period of acclimatization and then dragged him—too awed to protest much—into her fearsome regimen of self-improvement. Every bitter Scandinavian winter morning, before daybreak, in the huge, only half-heated library of her palace, Descartes tried to collect his numbed wits and hold forth on the wonders of philosophy and mathematics. But the inveterate 11 o'clock scholar lasted just 11 weeks. Then, at the age of 54, he contracted influenza and died, proving that his own lifelong care of himself had been right and the headstrong queen wrong.

The year was 1650, when Descartes' colleagues had already begun to flesh out the bones of *La Géométrie*. At that time an eight-year-old named Isaac Newton was flying kites with lanterns in them to scare the villagers of North Witham in Lincolnshire, England. And this child, scant years later, was to turn analytic geometry into the most practical mathematics ever invented—calculus, the mathematics of movement.

The Mathematics of Beauty in Nature and Art

In the 13th Century, Thomas Aquinas stated a fundamental truth of esthetics: "The senses delight in things duly proportioned." St. Thomas was expressing the direct and very often measurable relationship that exists between beauty and mathematics, a relationship that applies to both natural beauty and man's art. It appears that nothing in nature is so small or seemingly insignificant that it does not merit a pleasing symmetry, as is evidenced by the morning-glory buds opposite, formed into two trim spirals. Furthermore, there are numberless other examples—the endlessly embellished hexagons of the snowflake, the lovely geometric spiral of the chambered nautilus, the perfect cubes found in mineral crystals. As for man, himself a remarkably symmetrical creation, he appears to react instinctively and positively to forms which follow rigid geometric rules—both in what he sees around him and in his own creative acts of art and architecture.

TWO LIVING CORKSCREWS
A pair of delicately tinted morning-glory buds spiral upward in the sunlight like two tiny, waxen corkscrews. Spirals, whether in plants or animals, seem to be a favored shape in nature *(page 93)*. However, the graceful convolutions of these buds are only a transitory state, for within another two days they will disappear, gradually unfolding into the familiar trumpet-shaped flowers of summer.

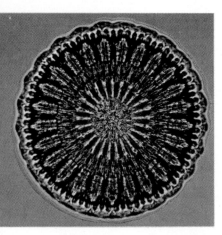

A CIRCULAR PLANT
The diatom, a microscopic sea plant with the mosaic beauty of a stained-glass window, is a nearly perfect circle with ribbed radii for added strength.

A TRIANGULAR GEM
The cross section of a semiprecious tourmaline, mined in Madagascar, reveals the stone's prismatic structure as a series of neatly nested triangles.

A CUBED CRYSTAL
A sample of pyrite, or iron disulphide, often called fool's gold, occurs as a series of interlocking cubes. Common table salt also is made of cubic crystals.

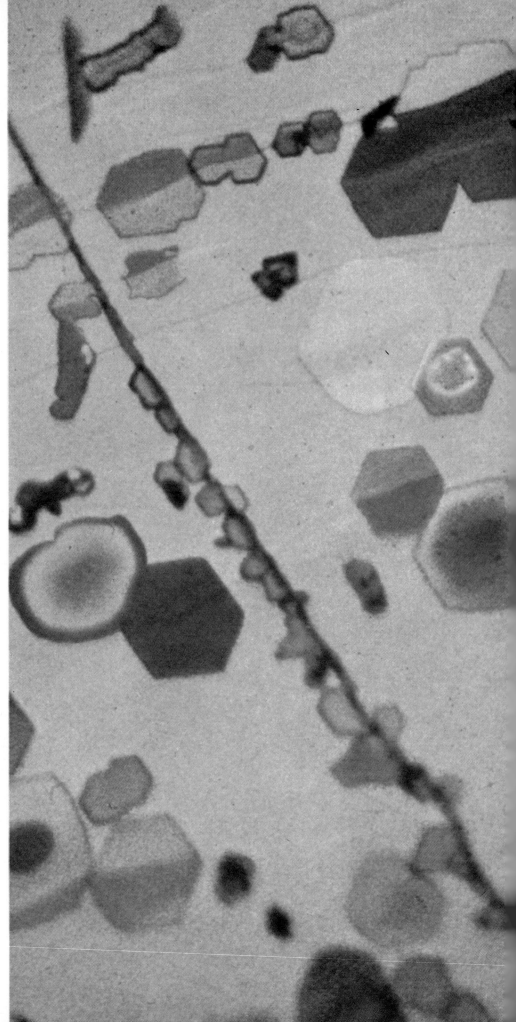

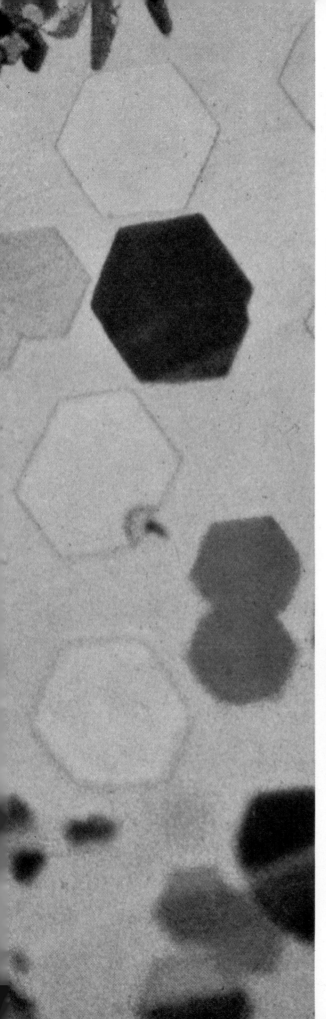

The common starfish is a pentagram, but some species have six points.

The Pleasing Geometry of Nature's Creations

Nature seems to delight in the creation of varied geometric shapes. Its figures come in circles, triangles, cubes, hexagons and even stars. But these constitute only the barest and most simple beginnings. Common mineral quartz, for example, often occurs as a trigonal trapezohedron—that is, a crystal structure roughly made up in a triangular arrangement, whose individual faces are four-sided. Even the most simple forms may mask complexity. Ordinary hexagonal-shaped snow crystals *(left)* can group themselves to form a snowflake of such intricacy that no geometrician would attempt to assign it a name.

SIX-SIDED SNOW
A remarkable photograph shows several hexagonal snow crystals before they begin to cluster themselves to form the familiar six-spoked flakes.

SIX-SIDED CELLS
A honeycomb cross section consists of a series of hexagons, which are not only strong, but also allow the most storage within the available space.

A SPIRALED FLOWER

The diagram above reveals the double spiraling of the daisy head at right. Two opposite sets of rotating spirals are formed by the arrangement of the individual florets in the head. They are also near-perfect equiangular spirals. There are 21 in the clockwise direction and 34 counterclockwise. This 21:34 ratio is composed of two adjacent terms in the mysterious Fibonacci sequence.

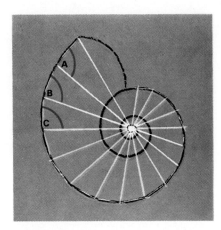

A SPIRALED SHELL

The cutaway of a chambered nautilus shell (opposite) shows its compartments. Only the outermost is the animal's home at any given time. Collectively, these chambers form an equiangular spiral: the black spiral intersects all of the white radii at exactly the same angle, so that the angles A, B, C and so on around the shell are always identical to one another.

The Mysterious Mathematics of Nature's Spirals

Nature never has been content with simple shapes, but has created all kinds of intricate mathematical designs, including a variety of spirals. For example, the shell of the chambered nautilus (opposite) is an equiangular, or logarithmic, spiral: as can be seen in the diagram, the curve of the spiral always intersects the outreaching radii at a fixed angle. Logarithmic spirals also occur in the curve of elephants' tusks, the horns of wild sheep and even canaries' claws. Similar, though less precise, spirals are formed by the tiny florets in the core of daisy blossoms (above). The eye sees these spirals (diagram at upper left) as two distinct sets, radiating clockwise and counterclockwise, with each set always made up of a predetermined number of

spirals. Most daisies have 21 and 34. Similar arrangements of opposing spirals are found in pine-cone scales (5 one way, 8 the other), the bumps on pineapples (8 and 13) and the leaves of many trees.

This phenomenon is made all the more mysterious by its relationship with a certain mathematical sequence known by the nickname of its medieval discoverer, Leonardo ("Fibonacci") da Pisa. The Fibonacci sequence is produced by starting with 1 and adding the last two numbers to arrive at the next: 1, 1, 2, 3, 5, 8, 13, 21, 34, etc. The daisy's spiral ratio of 21:34 corresponds to two adjacent Fibonacci numbers, as do the pine cone's 5:8 and the pineapple's 8:13—and the same is true of many other plants with a spiral leaf-growth pattern.

A Golden Rule for the World's Architecture

Fibonacci numbers, besides bearing a curious relationship to botany, also appear to exert a strange influence on art and architecture. The ratio between any two adjacent Fibonacci numbers after 3 is about 1:1.6. This is the so-called Golden Ratio, or Golden Section, which has intrigued experts for centuries because of its connection with esthetics. The ratio—expressed more precisely as 1:1.618—occurs in pentagons, circles and decagons—but notably in the Golden Rectangle, a figure whose two sides bear the magic relationship to each other.

The Golden Rectangle is said to be one of the most visually satisfying of all geometric forms; for years experts have been finding examples in everything from the edifices of ancient Greece to art masterpieces. In recent times the validity of its link to beauty has been widely debated. Nevertheless, as the pictures on these pages clearly indicate, the Golden Rectangle occurs in art more often than can be accounted for by mere coincidence.

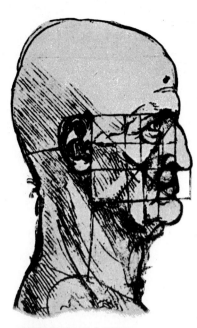

SYMMETRY IN A FACE
In Leonardo da Vinci's drawing of an old man, probably a self-portrait, the artist has overlaid the picture with a square subdivided into rectangles, some of which approximate Golden Rectangles. There is no way of telling whether Da Vinci's grid work governs or follows the proportions of the face—but he once helped to illustrate a book which dealt with properties of the golden proportions.

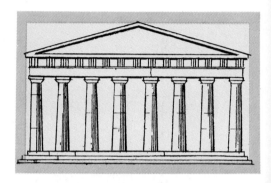

IN AN ANCIENT TEMPLE
The Parthenon at Athens *(right)* fits into a Golden Rectangle almost precisely once its ruined triangular pediment is drawn in *(above)*. Though it incorporates many geometric balances, its builders in the Fifth Century B.C. probably had no conscious knowledge of the Golden Ratio.

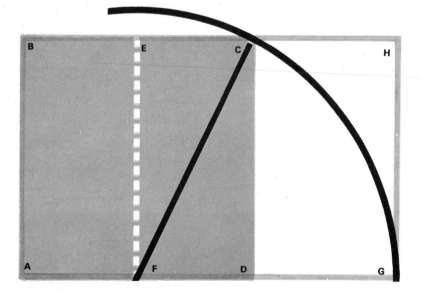

THE GOLDEN RECTANGLE
The geometric construction of a Golden Rectangle begins with a square *(in blue),* which is then divided in two equal parts by the dotted line EF. Point F now serves as the center of a circle whose radius is the diagonal FC. An arc of the circle is drawn (CG) and the base line AD is extended to intersect it. This becomes the base of the rectangle. The new side HG is now drawn at right angles to the new base, with the line BH brought out to meet it. The resultant Golden Rectangle has one unusual property: if the original square is taken away, what remains will still be a Golden Rectangle.

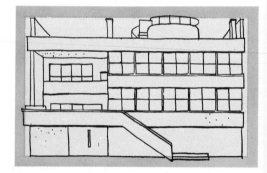

IN A MODERN VILLA
This home in suburban Paris represents the conscious use of the Golden Rectangle. The rectangle exists not only in the over-all design above but also vertically in the area to the left of the stairs. Le Corbusier, the architect, felt that human life was "comforted" by mathematics.

"RECREATIONS" OF DA VINCI

St. Jerome, an unfinished canvas by Leonardo da Vinci painted about 1483, shows the great scholar with a lion lying at his feet. A Golden Rectangle (black overlay) fits so neatly around St. Jerome that some experts believe Leonardo purposely painted the figure to conform to those proportions. Such an approach would have been in keeping with the artist's ardent interest in mathematics. He took special delight in what he once described as "geometrical recreations."

GOLDEN DOTS OF SEURAT

La Parade, painted in the characteristic multi-dotted style of the French impressionist Georges Seurat, contains numerous examples of Golden proportions. A nearly perfect Golden Rectangle lies within the points A, B, C and D. Golden Sections (that is, lines divided in the mystic ratio of 1 to 1.618) are to be found in the relationships of GF to FA, FE to EA and GH to HI. According to one art expert, Seurat "attacked every canvas by the Golden Section."

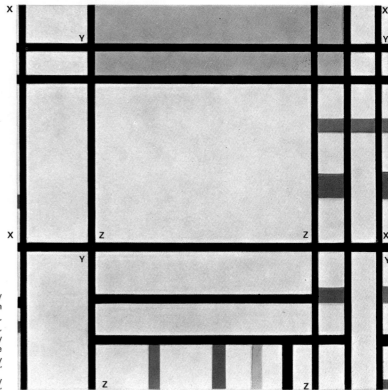

INVISIBLE SQUARES OF MONDRIAN

Place de la Concorde, a linear abstraction by Piet Mondrian, incorporates overlapping Golden Rectangles. At least three are readily apparent, one indicated at its four corners by the letter X, another by Y and the third by Z. They probably are inadvertent; Mondrian himself was vague about the design of his paintings, saying only that his aim was the "destruction of volume." Asked if he always painted squares, his reply was: "Squares? I see no squares in my pictures."

A SCENE SANS PERSPECTIVE
In this 12th Century illumination, which has no mathematical perspective, the castle is dwarfed by the six boatloads of attacking warriors. And the boats at the top of the picture, supposedly a great distance off on the horizon, appear to be just as large as the vessels in the foreground.

A PLAN FOR PERSPECTIVE
The rule of optical perspective begins with the horizon line (ABC). One point, B, is established as the principal vanishing point, and all lines receding directly from the viewer are made to converge at that point. All other lines except verticals and parallels to the horizon have their own individual vanishing points, governed by their particular angle to the plane of the picture. The vanishing point for the rectangle at left is point A, for the cube at right, point C.

Canaletto's *Stairs of Santa Maria della Salute* is a masterpiece of perspective in contrast to

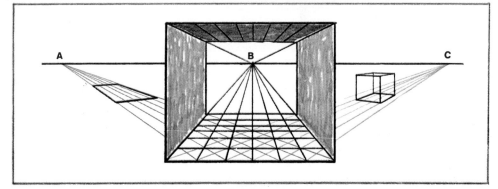

the small picture at upper left. The principal vanishing point can be found by extending the line of the stone quay back to the horizon.

Perspective, the Geometry of the Artist

Amid the fascination with mathematics in the Renaissance, painters became more aware of geometry's vital role in achieving optical perspective—the quality which gives a painting three-dimensional depth. Until then, painting had been primarily "conceptual," with the most important subject given most prominent treatment even if this distorted the picture, as in the scene at left, above. Not only the idea of perspective but the word itself came into wide use during the Renaissance. It derives from the Latin for "seen through" —reflecting the concept that a picture with optical focus was really a geometrically governed "window in space" *(left)*.

99

PERSPECTIVE IN DISTORTION

The technical ability to depict perspective is carried to extremes in this reflection-viewed 18th Century painting. The picture itself is completely distorted. But viewed by means of a lamp-chimney-shaped mirror, the images take form—two ladies and a servant, serenaded by a musician. The process, called anamorphosis, was popular from about 1550 to 1850. Secrets of the technique are unknown. The artist probably never looked directly at the canvas, but drew his distortions with his hand guided only by the reflections of his work in the mirror.

A Dürer woodcut shows an artist peering through a glass grid to study foreshortening.

Masterworks and Fun, Products of a Maturing Technique

The first attempts at mathematical perspective came out of the seething intellectual climate of 15th Century Florence. But from there the technique for creating solid reality on flat canvas spread rapidly through Europe. And as it spread, new masters added virtuoso touches.

The first great exponent of perspective north of the Alps was Albrecht Dürer. This great German artist imagined the canvas as a glass screen through which the world is seen. In the woodcut above he shows how an artist can literally copy on ruled paper the image he observes through an identically ruled glass pane. By 1700 the laws of perspective were so familiar that artists were amusing themselves and clients with exhibitionistic works like the one at left, and even engaging in gentle spoofs of their craft *(below)*.

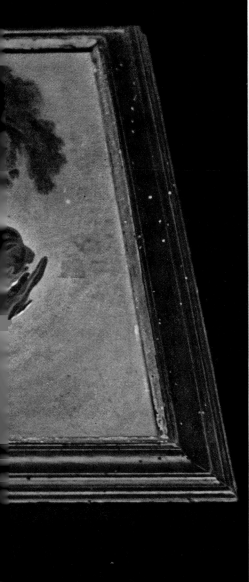

DISTORTION OF PERSPECTIVE
False Perspective is William Hogarth's 1754 travesty of mishandled perspective. The fisherman in the foreground calmly dips his line in a distant stream, and the woman leaning from the window *(upper right)* has no difficulty lighting the pipe of the man on a remote hilltop.

The Legacy of Nature to the Master Builders

Since Nature long ago created most basic geometric shapes, man's own creations are inevitably imitative. Man's great contribution, especially in the field of architecture, has been his imaginative use of these many shapes. Architect Frank Lloyd Wright, for example, reflects the helical spiral of the nautilus in his design of a museum *(right)*. And Buckminster Fuller, in his famous domes, utilized thousands of simple equilateral triangles linked together to obtain the shortest, strongest route—the geodesic—across the dome's spherical surface. The result, in both cases, is a marriage of mathematics' utility and beauty that Nature herself might envy.

A SPIRAL SHOWCASE

The curving lines of New York's Guggenheim Museum spiral upward in massive poured concrete. With this helix design, architect Wright was able to achieve, on a base 100 feet in diameter, a gently sloping interior ramp more than a quarter mile long, for the advantageous display of art.

A sphere made of equilateral triangles comprises the geodesic dome for this hillside home constructed against a Los Angeles backdrop.

5

Mastering
the Mysteries
of Movement

NOTHING in the world is immune from change. The hardest rock on the driest desert expands or contracts in the shifting sunlight. The steel gauge blocks at the National Bureau of Standards, even though they are stored in temperature-controlled subterranean vaults, are subject to seasonal fluctuations in length thought to be caused by radiation from the surrounding walls. Everything grows or shrinks, warms up or cools down, changes its position, its color, its composition—perhaps even its spots.

Inescapable as the process of change is, and vital as it is to understanding the laws of nature, it is difficult to analyze. Being continuous, it offers no easy point at which the mind can catch it and pin it down. For centuries it baffled mathematicians. Some starts, to be sure, were made toward a mathematics of movement. The Greeks did so when they thought of curves as tracings made by moving points, and when they analyzed curving lines, instant by instant, through the technique of slicing them into infinitesimally fine segments. Descartes did so when he conceived of the items in an equation as functions between *variables*, and most of all when he supplied a way to draw graph-pictures of *fluid* situations and relationships. But by and large the world of mathematics was populated by waxworks—shapes and numbers that stood stock-still.

Then, in 1665 and 1666, England's incomparable Isaac Newton produced a prodigious brain child, now called calculus, which for the first time permitted the mathematical analysis of all movement and change. In calculus Newton combined the fine-slicing technique of the Greeks and the graph system of Descartes to devise a marvelously automatic mental tool for operating on an equation in order to get at infinitesimals. So quickly did calculus prove its effectiveness that in a few years its creator used it to work out the laws of motion and gravitation—the fundamental laws of physics which explain why the solar system acts as it does, or why any moving object reacts as it does to outside forces like gravity, the tension of a spring or the push of a man's hand. By its ability to probe the fleeting mysteries of movement, calculus today has become the principal pipeline between practical science and the reservoir of mathematical thought. Every airplane, every television set, every bridge, every bomb, every spacecraft owes it a tithe of indebtedness.

The different kinds of change which calculus can analyze are as diverse as a queen's wardrobe. If the factors involved in any fluid situation can be put in terms of an equation, then calculus can get at them and uncover the laws they obey. The change under scrutiny may be as dramatic as the gathering speed of a missile lifting from its pad or as quiet as the varying grade of a mountain road. It may be as visible as the pounds added around a once-svelte waistline or as invisible as the ebb and flow of current in a power line. It may be as audible as the crescendo of a Bee-

STOPPING MOTION IN MID-AIR
This superspeed photograph of a man swinging
Indian clubs—"stopping" the clubs at
successive instants throughout the swing—
was taken by Professor Harold Edgerton of
M.I.T. In an analogous way, calculus is used to
"stop" complex movements mathematically, and
to analyze a changing process instant by instant.

thoven concerto or as silent as the build-up of flood force behind a dam.

Calculus analyzes all these situations by invoking two new mathematical processes—the first fundamental operations to be added to the canon of mathematics since the laws of addition, subtraction, multiplication, division and finding roots were laid down some 4,000 years ago. These new operations are called *differentiation* and *integration,* and they are the reverse of each other in much the same way that subtraction is the reverse of addition, or division of multiplication. Differentiation is a way of computing the rate at which one variable in a situation changes in relation to another at any point in a process—at a given instant in time, for example, or at a given point in space. The actual method employed in differentiation is to divide a small change in one variable by a small change in another; to let these changes both shrink until they approach zero; then—and this is the key—to find the value which the ratio between them approaches as the changes become indefinitely small. This value is what mathematicians call a "limit," and it is the answer they are seeking, the end result of differentiation—the rate of change at a given instant or point. Integration works back the other way from differentiation; it takes an equation in terms of rate of change and converts it into an equation in terms of the variables that do the changing.

Through differentiation, a mathematician can probe deep into a fluid situation until he finds some unchanging factor that reflects the action of a constant law of nature. In this fashion Newton and later theorists made a discovery which is still not easy for laymen to absorb. This discovery was that the constant factor in many processes of nature is the rate at which a rate of change changes. Deciphering this seeming double talk may appear hopeless. But anyone who drives a car is familiar with the rate of change of a rate of change whether he realizes it or not. The speed of the car—so many miles per hour—is a rate of change of distance with respect to time. In speeding up or slowing down, the car's speed itself changes, and changes at a rate—acceleration or deceleration—which is the rate of change of the rate of change.

In nature, gravity acts to make a falling object move at a rate which increases at a constant rate. For processes involving actual physical movement, Newton defined this rate of a rate as the *acceleration.* And he called the gravity causing it a *force.* He defined force in general as something which causes an object to accelerate. As applied through calculus, this definition—laid down three centuries ago—has enabled scientists to do no less than identify the three fundamental forces of the cosmos: the force of gravitation; the force of magnetism, or electric charge; and the force that binds together the atomic nucleus.

In contrast to the spectacular role that calculus has played in unlocking the secrets of the universe, the nomenclature surrounding differen-

TWO GIANTS, ONE INVENTION

MASTER OF MATH AND MINT
Though a mathematical genius, Isaac Newton devoted much of his life to theological study and, in later years, to his job as master of the mint. He developed his version of calculus in 1665 but did not publish his findings until 1704.

A GENIUS IN MANY REALMS
Gottfried Wilhelm von Leibniz was a universal genius who won varying degrees of honor in law, religion, statecraft, history, literature, logic, metaphysics and speculative philosophy. He published his version of calculus in 1684.

tiation and integration is woefully prosaic. The rate of change of a y or x, found by differentiation, is called a *derivative*—a derivative of y with respect to x, written dy/dx, or of x with respect to y, written dx/dy. A derivative's counterpart, found by integration, is called an *integral*, and is symbolized by $\int$, an elongated letter S, which was short, originally, for "sum" or "summation." When integration is performed on an equation written in terms of derivatives, it converts the equation back into one in which the x and y have doffed their rate-of-change disguises and resumed normal algebraic appearance.

A definition for dieters

The handles and hieroglyphs attached to the techniques of calculus may look alien, but the ideas behind them are easily recognized. Being a rate of change, a derivative means, simply, the speed of a process: so many miles per hour or feet per second if it refers to change in position; so many pounds per week if it refers to a triumph in dieting; so many geniuses per childbirth if it refers to I.Q. statistics; so much cornstalk per candle power of sunshine if it refers to the growth of a corn crop. The integral corresponding to each of these derivatives would be the miles traveled, pounds lost, geniuses gained or length of cornstalk grown.

When used abstractly in an equation, a derivative can most readily be thought of in terms of the curve which represents this equation on a graph. At any point, the curve is rising or falling at a rate of so many y-units per x-unit. This slope up or down is the exact geometric equivalent of the rate of change—the derivative—of y with respect to x. Engineers often express the grade of a hill, the pitch of a roof or the steepness of an airplane's climb in identical terms: as so much altitude gained per unit of horizontal distance traversed. But in these applications the slope is normally conceived of as being measured over some definite span of distance. In calculus, on the other hand, the derivative is thought of as an instantaneous slope at a single point on a curve.

That this elusive concept of instantaneous slope is no figment of the mathematical imagination can be seen in an artillery shell as it arcs toward target. At any single moment the shell is moving in a definite direction. This direction is an instantaneous slope with respect to the ground, a rate of change in the shell's altitude with respect to its horizontal position. In terms of a graph, the speed of the shell, moving up or down, can also be considered as an instantaneous slope on a curve—a rate of change in the shell's altitude with respect to the time that has been elapsing since the shell was fired. A mathematician would normally write such a derivative—the velocity of climb or fall, or the rate of change of vertical distance—as dy/dt, in which the t stands for time.

The counterpart of a derivative, an integral, can also be visualized in

THE APPROXIMATE SUM
The 18th Century Swiss mathematician Leonhard Euler established the Greek sigma in calculus as the symbol for the sum of a *finite* number of rectangles approximating the area under a curve.

THE INFINITE INTEGRAL
Leibniz popularized the use of a tall S as a symbol in calculus for an integral, a sum composed of an *infinite* number of infinitely thin rectangles exactly measuring the area under a curve.

terms of a graph. Suppose that y equals some expression of x and that this equation is plotted as a curve. Then the integral of y is the area between the curve and the horizontal line, or axis, running along below it. Why this is so can be seen by imagining that the area under the curve is filled by a picket fence with a scalloped top (illustration on the page opposite). As the fence is being built, each new picket adds to the area of the fence. In fact, the height of each added picket is a measure of the rate at which the area of the fence is growing; a six-foot picket, for instance, adds twice as much area as a three-foot picket. The integral of the rate of change, therefore, must be the actual factor in the situation that is changing: namely, the area of the fence itself. The geometric equivalent of each picket is simply the height of a curve—the vertical, or y coordinate of each point on a curve. Integrating y must, therefore, give the total area under the curve.

Many of the most practical applications of calculus stem from integration's ability to sum up y-length pickets and determine areas. Through it a mathematician can determine the volume of all manner of irregular shapes, such as airplane fuselages or oil-storage tanks; he can also find the areas of curved surfaces—the amount of sheet metal in a molded car body or the lifting surface on the wings of a jet.

There is one major difficulty in the process of integration—a difficulty so enormous and so recurrent that most of our largest computers today have been built specifically to cope with it. This is the problem of so-called "boundary conditions." When the area of a picket fence is measured, the boundary conditions are established by the two pickets that mark the two ends of the fence. But there are no ends to many of the curves that represent equations. The area beneath this type of curve may be indefinitely large. To give it boundaries, the mathematician erects the equivalent of end posts to mark off the particular part of the area he is interested in. He then integrates the equation represented by the curve between these two verticals. Often, however, in the case of equations which are arrived at experimentally, the proper way to interpret such an equation cannot be found except by integrating it, and the boundary conditions necessary for integrating it cannot be found except by understanding how to interpret it. To avoid this impasse, the scientist, in effect, chooses arbitrary picket posts and lets a computer run off dozens of laborious solutions, which give him insight into the equation and the process of change which it symbolizes.

To work out the rules of calculus, Newton visualized what would happen if one point on a graph-curve slid down into a point nearby. As the slide begins, the average slope of the curve between the two points is the number of y-units separating them vertically, divided by the number of x-units separating them horizontally. As the slide continues, both

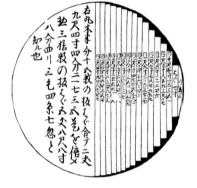

EARLY ORIENTAL CALCULUS
A Japanese calculus, traditionally credited to the 17th Century mathematician Seki Kōwa, was called *yenri* (circle principle). The above illustration of crude integration was drawn in 1670 by one of Seki Kōwa's pupils. It measures the circle area with a series of rectangles.

FINDING A MILITARY MAXIMUM
A curious fact of warfare for which calculus has formal proof is that to reach maximum range with a cannon, the muzzle must be set at 45° *(opposite, left)*. As the diagram opposite right shows, if a gun is elevated above 45°, the trajectory is wasted on too high a ride, while below 45°, gravity pulls the shell to earth too soon. Calculus made it possible to analyze the various trajectories, proving the one at 45° the most effective.

distances in this fraction diminish toward zero and finally vanish when the two points merge. But this does not mean that the fraction itself vanishes. A ratio of 1:2, for instance, need not suddenly become zero just because its numerator and denominator become indefinitely small. When last heard from, as they disappear arm in arm into the fastnesses of infinity, the numerator may be one zillionth and the denominator two zillionths, but the ratio between them is still 1 to 2.

Finding the value which a fraction approaches as its numerator and denominator both diminish toward nothingness is called "taking a limit." If the numerator equals half the denominator, the limit is one half. If the numerator equals 10 times the denominator, the limit is 10. As two points on a curve slide together, the vertical and horizontal distances between them remain coupled, even as they fade away, by the relationship of y to x expressed in the original equation of the curve. As they merge, therefore, the ratio of their distances approaches a definite limit which can be evaluated in terms of y and x. This limit, 1/2 or 10 or whatever it may be, is the slope of the curve at the precise spot where the two points merge—the rate of change of vertical y with respect to horizontal x or, put another way, the derivative of y with respect to x.

The subtle train of reasoning which enabled Newton to differentiate equations and find the derivative or limiting value of the ratio—written dy/dx or dy/dt—is the fundamental process of calculus. It can be roughly paraphrased as follows: in a developing situation, the difference between the state of affairs at one moment and the state of affairs at the next moment is an indication of how the situation is shaping up; and if the ratio of the net changes that take place between the two moments is evaluated as a limit—a limit approached when the interval between the two moments is imagined as diminishing toward zero—then that limit shows how fast developments are taking place. The logic of calculus can be applied to moments of time, points on a curve, temperatures in a gas or any state of affairs which can be related by equations; the same rules of differentiation apply to all of them.

A simple gift from Galileo

The way these rules work, and the reason for their enormous usefulness, can best be illustrated by applying them to the classically simple equation $y = 16t^2$, devised by the renowned Italian astronomer and physicist, Galileo Galilei. This brief, unpretentious expression is one of the most versatile in all physics because it shows how gravity acts on a freely falling object—an elevator run amuck, a hailstone or a jumper descending to ground. Since almost all movements and changes on earth are heavily influenced by gravity, the equation of free fall indirectly plays a part in innumerable human actions—from taking a step or lob-

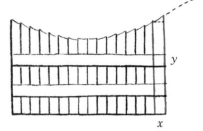

PICKET-FENCE INTEGRALS
A picket fence is a simple key to integration. As shown, the area added by one new picket is roughly the rectangle $x \times y$. This leaves out the triangular top of the picket, however. Calculus solves the problem by making the pickets so thin the tops become negligible.

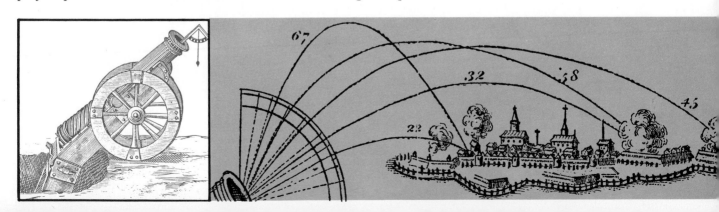

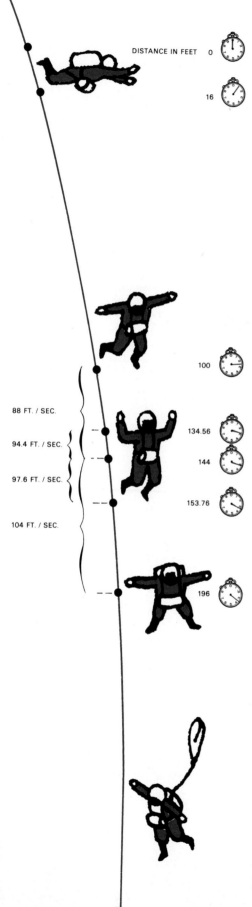

DISTANCE IN FEET   0

16

100

88 FT. / SEC.

94.4 FT. / SEC.   134.56

144

97.6 FT. / SEC.

153.76

104 FT. / SEC.

196

bing a tennis ball to lifting a steel girder or launching an astronaut into orbit.

Timing an object as it falls from a given height is the most straightforward method of gauging the effects of gravity. It was this technique which Galileo used, about 1585, to arrive at his free-fall equation. According to legend, Galileo dropped small cannon balls from the colonnades of the leaning tower of Pisa. According to his own account, he used the less fanciful means of timing cannon balls as they rolled down a ramp. In any event, Galileo ascertained that the equation for free fall was $y = 16t^2$, with y representing the distance fallen in feet and t the elapsed time in seconds after the start of the fall.

By differentiating this equation twice—so as to shave away successive layers of change and inconstancy—Newton uncovered the essential nature of gravitation. Differentiating the equation once, he found that the speed with which a jumper is falling at any moment equals 32 times the number of seconds which he has been falling. Differentiating the equation a second time, he found that the jumper's acceleration—the rate of increase in his speed—is always 32 feet per second, every second.

The fact that in the free-fall equation acceleration equals a constant number, 32, indicates the end of the trail. This 32 need not be differentiated further; it does not change, and its rate of change is zero. It represents a law of nature: that every free-falling object falls to earth with a constant acceleration of 32 feet per second, every second.

Having ascertained this fact by calculus, Newton was able to set his mathematical sights far beyond the earth and to deduce the law of universal gravitation—one of the most important results ever to be achieved by mathematics. It is the law which governs the movements of all celestial bodies—from human beings in orbit to entire systems of stars.

Looking back with awe on what a little deduction could accomplish in the mind of Isaac Newton, later thinkers have ranked him as the greatest physicist and one of the greatest mathematicians the world has ever known. Albert Einstein wrote: "Nature to him was an open book, whose letters he could read without effort." Newton himself said: "I do not know what I may appear to the world; but to myself I seem to have been only like a boy playing on the seashore, and diverting myself in now and then finding a smoother pebble or a prettier shell than ordinary, whilst the great ocean of truth lay all undiscovered before me."

Newton began to use his astounding inventiveness while still a child, to build toys for himself, including a wooden water clock that actually kept time and a flour mill worked by a mouse. His brilliance did not really catch fire, however, until he read Euclid at the late age of 19. The story goes that he rushed impatiently on to Descartes' relatively abstruse *La Géométrie*. Thereafter his progress was meteoric. Five years

MEASURING A FREE FALL
A parachutist in free fall drops faster every moment. Calculus finds his rate at any instant by, in effect, measuring shorter and shorter time segments. In the first bracketed period *(left)*, he falls at an average speed of 88 feet per second for half a second, in the next equal period 104 feet. In two shorter periods, he drops 94.4 feet per second and 97.6 feet. The ever-narrowing rates finally converge to 96 feet per second at exactly three seconds.

later, while still a graduate student at Cambridge, he had already worked out the basic operations of calculus—the rules of integration and differentiation, which he called the laws of "fluxions and fluents."

Newton put together his great invention and applied it in a preliminary way to the problems of motion and gravitation in a two-year burst of creativity, while rusticating during the epidemic of plague which swept England in 1665 and 1666. In retrospect it seems as if the whole framework of modern science arose from his mind as miraculously as a jinni from a bottle. But as Newton himself said, he "stood on the shoulders of giants." Many men had wrestled with the same problems; it was his genius to fuse their separate inspirations. The twin processes of differentiation and integration in calculus, for instance, were rooted in two classic questions of Greek antiquity: how to construct a tangent line (a line that just touches a curve at a given point), and how to calculate an area which is bounded on one side by a curve. The problem of the tangent, or "touching" line, was equivalent to the problem of finding the slope of a curve at any point and therefore of finding the derivative of an equation. The area problem was equivalent to the problem of integrating the equation that gives the rate of growth of an area.

A wine keg of infinitesimals

By viewing any curve as a succession of infinitely short segments, or any area as an accumulation of infinitely fine slices, the Greeks—particularly Archimedes—had solved a number of specific problems concerning rates of change. Mathematicians of the 16th and 17th Centuries also used infinitesimal methods, though seldom with rigorous Greek proofs. Kepler, for instance, had employed infinitesimals to give vintners a formula for gauging the volume of wine kegs. In Descartes' time and in the 15 years after his death, his compatriot, Pierre de Fermat, and the Englishman, John Wallis, had begun to cast infinitesimals in the helpful analytic molds of equations. Then, in about 1663, Newton's professor at Cambridge, Isaac Barrow, became the first man to realize that the tangent problem and the area problem are two sides of the same coin—in effect, that integration is the reverse of differentiation.

When Newton first began to unite all these preliminary insights in the single well-knit structure of calculus, he showed Barrow some of his early results. Barrow was so enthusiastic that he generously let it be known about Cambridge that Newton had done what he himself had failed to do. A few years later, in 1669, when he was retiring, he was instrumental in getting Newton, then 26, appointed as his successor to the Lucasian professorship of mathematics at the university—one of the most desirable chairs of mathematical scholarship in the academic world. Thereafter, honors and inspirations came to Newton in a steady

A PAGE OF A MASTERWORK
The great scientific questions of Newton's time concerned the motions of heavenly bodies. Building on such work as Kepler's, shown below, Newton developed a system of planetary motion and, in the process, invented calculus. His findings were published in his *Principia*. A page of this monumental work plotting the orbits of the earth and moon is shown above.

A PRODUCT OF CRUDE CALCULUS
Johannes Kepler, some 50 years before Newton, used a crude, geometric calculus to devise his three laws of planetary motion. In the second law, illustrated here, he proved that a planet changes its speed according to its distance from the sun, and the line joining the planet to the sun sweeps out equal areas in equal times. Thus, at right, the planet's time of travel from each point to the next is the same and the two tinted areas ASJ and DSE are equal.

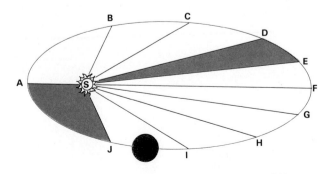

111

MENTOR TO A GENIUS
The English mathematician and theologian Isaac Barrow taught Newton at Cambridge. He aided the young genius in building calculus and also had him made successor to his professorship.

GADFLY TO AN AUTHOR
Oxford professor John Wallis invented the sign ∞ to designate infinity, helped to develop calculus and pressed hard to persuade Newton to publish "these notions about fluxions."

stream. Over the next four decades he formulated the law of gravitation and used it to explain the movements of the planets, moon and tides; analyzed the color spectrum of light; constructed the first modern reflecting telescope; performed innumerable alchemistic experiments; tried to reconcile with Scripture the date of 4004 B.C., which was currently accepted as the time of Adam's creation; served as a member of Parliament; was appointed warden and then master of the British mint; was knighted by Queen Anne in 1705 and was repeatedly elected president of Britain's select scientific club, the Royal Society, from 1703 until his death in 1727.

Strangely enough, Newton revealed his monumental discoveries to only a few of his scientific cronies. Many explanations have been given for his inordinate secretiveness. It has been said that he was always too busy with new ideas to find time to write up old ones, and that he had a passionate distaste for the wrangles and criticism which inevitably raged around scientific pronouncements in those days. Then, too, he was just not much of a talker. While he was in Parliament, his only recorded utterance was a request to open the window. On one occasion the astronomer Edmund Halley came to him, after a discussion with England's most eminent scientists, to ask if he knew what path a planet would take around the sun if the only force influencing it was a force that diminishes according to the square of its distance from the sun. Newton immediately gave the answer: the path would be elliptical. When asked how he knew, he explained casually that he had worked out the problem years before as a graduate student. In other words, he had worked out the fundamental law of the universe and told nobody about it. Encouraged by Halley to re-create his original calculations, he went on to produce his masterwork, the *Principia.*

Newton's *Principia* is generally recognized as the most influential, conclusive and revolutionary scientific work ever to appear in print. In it, he not only explained why the solar system works the way it does but also laid down the laws of dynamics which are still the chief ingredients of practical engineering physics—of missile shoots or thruway construction. Most of these laws Newton had worked out through calculus, but like Archimedes before him, he chose to present his finished work in universally understood mathematics—as a lengthy Greek proof, couched almost entirely in the terms of classical geometry.

Not even the skillful coaxings of Halley could convince Newton to publish his calculus—not, that is, until another mathematician, the German Gottfried Wilhelm von Leibniz, had independently re-created the entire mental machinery. Leibniz invented calculus 10 years after Newton, in 1675, and in 1684 published his account of it, 20 years before Newton was to give the first published explanation of his own version.

Like Newton, Leibniz was as successful and practical as the mathematics he originated. The son of a well-to-do university professor, he learned Greek and Latin by the age of 12, attended university, took a law degree, and went on to become the counsel to kings and princes in an illustrious career that sometimes verged on the shady. He traveled all over Europe tracing dubious lineages to establish the dubious rights of princelings to vacant thrones. He formulated many of our modern principles of international power politics—including the phrase "balance of power." During trips to Paris, he studied algebra and analytic geometry under the great optical physicist Christian Huygens. And while jogging along in coaches on diplomatic missions, he created new mathematics simply for pleasure, including his own version of calculus.

Although Newton accomplished far more with calculus than Leibniz did, Leibniz had a superior notation for it—one he polished so carefully that we still use it. It was Leibniz who first wrote derivatives as dy/dx or dx/dy—forms that suggest the fractional rate-of-change measurements to which they apply. (Newton wrote the derivative of y as $\dot{y}$ and the derivative of x as $\dot{x}$. The dots in Newton's symbolism led rebellious 19th Century Cambridge students to protest against the "dotage" of English notation and to advocate the "pure d-ism" of continental notation.)

Unfortunately, Newton and Leibniz in their later years became embroiled in a chauvinistic dispute as to who had invented what first. The result was that scholars on the continent, helped by Leibniz' notation, went on to develop calculus further, while English mathematicians, hampered by the less felicitous notation devised by Newton, foundered in a morass of perplexities.

Salute to a lion's paw

The supremacy of the continental approach did not emerge, however, while Newton was still alive. At least twice after the rivalry had broken out, Leibniz and his followers posed problems with which they hoped to stump Newton. Each time Newton tossed off the answers in a single evening after coming home from his work at the mint. One of these problems was a particularly devilish one: to find the shape of the curve down which a bead will slide under the influence of gravity so as to move from a higher point to a lower point in the shortest possible time. The problem was important as an early example of "maximizing-minimizing" questions which confront mathematicians today—maximizing industrial productivity or minimizing the amount of fuel required to get to the moon. Newton solved the problem overnight and transmitted his solution anonymously the next morning through the channels of the Royal Society. Upon its receipt, Johann Bernoulli, the disciple of Leibniz who had posed the problem, is reported to have said, *"Tanquam ex ungue*

DETRACTOR OF NEWTON
Johann Bernoulli, one of eight mathematicians produced by a remarkable Swiss family in three generations, was loyal to Leibniz and hated Newton, did much to spread calculus in Europe.

CHAMPION OF LEIBNIZ
Jacob Bernoulli, a brother of Johann at top, was also a Leibniz supporter. He applied calculus to difficult questions of mechanics and introduced the calculus of variations.

leonem," which, freely translated, means "I recognize the lion by his paw."

Logicians of the next generation sharply criticized both Newton and Leibniz for having used the equivalents of infinitesimals—for having added up nothings to create the somethings of areas, and for having shaved down rates of change to instantaneous slopes measured in no time at all. The Irish metaphysician Bishop Berkeley, in an essay entitled "The Analyst," examined the logic of Newton's "fluxions" and concluded, "They are neither finite quantities, nor quantities infinitely small, nor yet nothing. May we not call them the ghosts of departed quantities. . .?"

Mathematicians of the 19th Century were to satisfy such critics by invoking new standards of rigor for calculus. But meanwhile it met the test of success—it worked. Scientific problems capitulated to it as the walls of Jericho to Joshua's trumpets. Indeed the chief danger was one of self-satisfaction. Using calculus, scientists explained every process in nature as a sequence of actions and reactions, of causes and effects. Nature, however, cannot be determined in this easy mechanical way. Anyone knows that there are slips between cup and lip—accidents in the forces which produce motion. But the laws of these accidents are also mathematical. And, as we shall see, mathematicians contemporaneous with Newton and Leibniz were working them out as the laws of chance.

Calculus: A Way of Probing the Changing World

When the great 17th Century mathematicians Isaac Newton and Gottfried Wilhelm von Leibniz developed calculus as a way of measuring motion, they were, in a sense, introducing to mathematics the principle of the motion picture. For just as a movie film consists of repeated still pictures of a moving object (as in the panels opposite), so does calculus break motion down into "stills" that can be observed "frame by frame." Once calculus was invented, mathematicians could treat a moving object as a point tracing a path through space and, by "stopping the action," calculate the object's speed and acceleration at a specific instant. This mathematics of motion became a fundamental scientific tool. The earth we stand on is in motion; so are the molecules of the air we breathe. With calculus such movements can be defined even though they cannot be seen. Although some of its abstractions are as difficult as anything in mathematics, calculus is based on a few simple ideas—function, approximation, rate of change, convergence, integration—which are explained on the following pages.

"STOPPING" THE FLIGHT OF A CAT
The famous sequence of photographs on the opposite page, showing a startled cat breaking into a run, was taken in 1887 by Eadweard Muybridge, inventor of a prototype motion-picture machine. These split-second pictures show that a continuous motion can be broken into small increments of change. In a similar way, calculus treats motion as an infinite number of "instants."

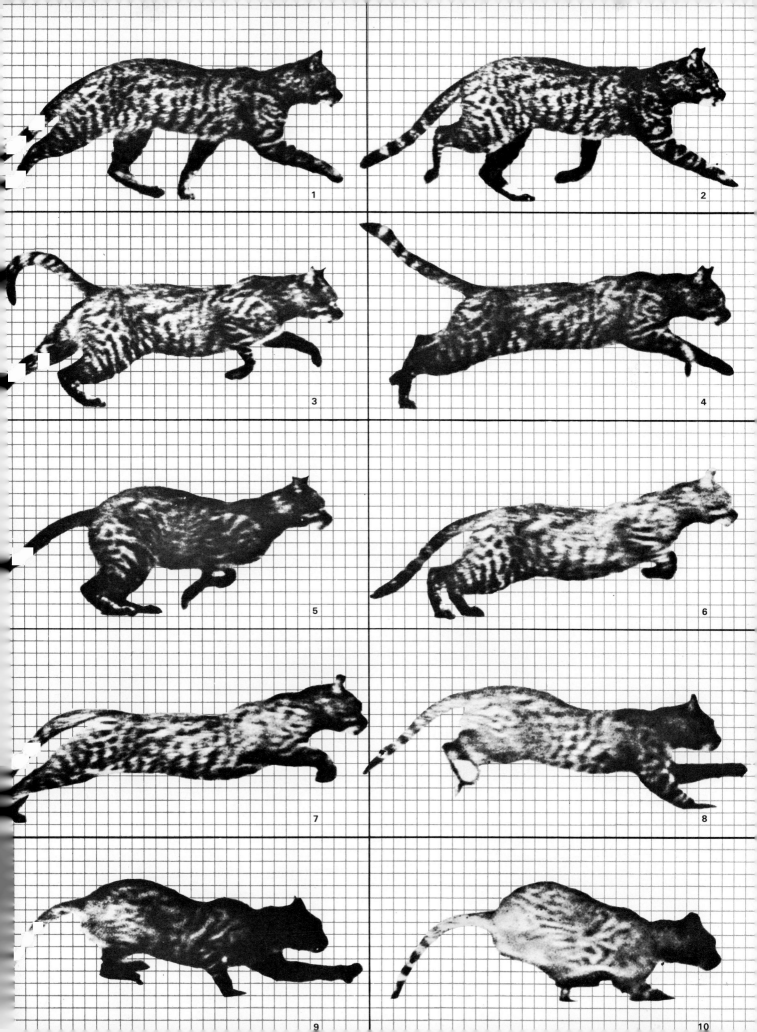

Weight as a function of calories is shown by a 277-pound Munich carpenter who daily consumes the amount on the table above.

FUNCTIONS

Charting the
Changes of a World
in Transition

The idea of "function," common to many branches of mathematics, is central to calculus. When a point moves along a path, the distance it travels is a function of—i.e., depends on—the time it takes. In general, one variable is a function of another if a change in one depends on a change in the other—as a boy's height is a function of his age *(right)*. This relationship can usually be written as an equation or drawn as a straight or curved line on a graph. Calculus can then be used to analyze the graph of a function—and thus the physical motion or change itself.

The analysis of functions is important because virtually everything in the world is undergoing some kind of transition. Metals, for example, expand when heated: thus the length of an iron bar is a function of its temperature. If its length when cold is known, the length when heated can be found once its temperature is determined. One everyday function is the cost of sending a letter by first-class mail. Once the rule (five cents for each ounce or fraction thereof) is known, its weight determines the amount of postage needed—i.e., postage is a function of weight.

Other functions useful in the space age are the relationship of the speed of a satellite to the diameter of its orbit, and the relationship of an astronaut's need for oxygen to his physical stress. The girth of the happy gourmand on the opposite page is a function of the six meals he eats every day. And the other pictures on these two pages also show common functions.

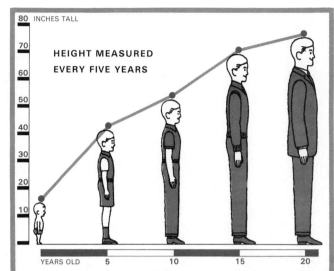

HEIGHT MEASURED
EVERY FIVE YEARS

80 INCHES TALL
70
60
50
40
30
20
10

YEARS OLD   5   10   15   20

Height as a function of age is demonstrated by the graph. The pictures show five-year intervals; the changing slope of the line shows that the rate of growth varies with age.

PRESSURE IN DEPTH
Water flowing from holes in a tin can illustrates a function important in physics: that water pressure changes with depth. The higher pressure at the lower holes of the can makes water squirt out in a flat trajectory; lower pressure at the upper holes produces a feeble stream.

The population of this resort is a function of the season. Coney Island, jammed during the summer *(left)*, is almost deserted in winter.

An approximation of the flight path of a plane taking off from an airport is shown by a special camera taking two pictures a second. The time

APPROXIMATION

Chopping Up a Curve
to Stop Action
and Measure a Moment

Change is inherent in the physical world: things "take shape," grow, move, speed up. Most changes occur at uneven rates: an airplane *(above)* picks up speed and rises faster toward the end of its climb than at the start. Just as it is possible to find the average rate of the plane's rise by dividing the total height of ascent by the time elapsed while rising, it is also possible to find the average rate of rise over any small interval, or "frame," of the process. But calculus can go further: it can make these "frames" so small that each one approximates a single point— i.e., a single instant in time. It is then possible to determine the precise rate of change that is taking place at that instant.

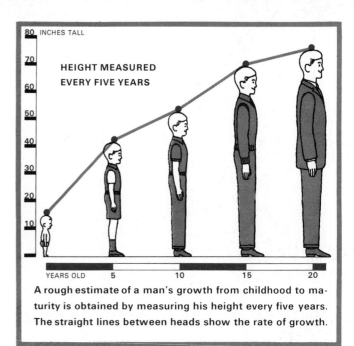

A rough estimate of a man's growth from childhood to maturity is obtained by measuring his height every five years. The straight lines between heads show the rate of growth.

118

is recorded by the clock at the bottom of the picture. Each of the photographs shows the plane at a single point on the curve of its take-off.

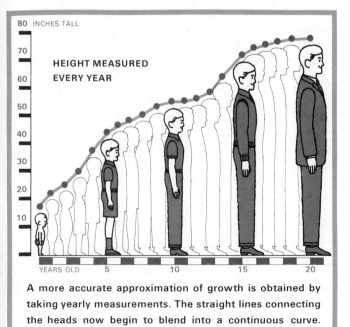

A more accurate approximation of growth is obtained by taking yearly measurements. The straight lines connecting the heads now begin to blend into a continuous curve.

Measurements taken every six months give a still more accurate rate-of-growth line. With increasingly smaller intervals, the lines merge into an ever-smoother curve.

THE STRAIN OF ACCELERATION

This striking sequence of pictures shows one visible effect of one rate of change: the distorted face of Colonel John Stapp, an Air Force doctor investigating the physical effects of acceleration by riding on a rocket sled. The picture at left shows Stapp before his ride starts. The next two pictures show his head thrown back and his face contorted by the wind blast as the sled picks up speed. The last pictures in the sequence show him thrown forward as the sled is braked to a stop with a deceleration equal to more than 40 times the force of gravity.

THE START OF ACCELERATION

Runners competing in the 1960 Olympic Games accelerate away from their starting blocks. Within three or four more strides the runners will be moving at top speed—which means that their acceleration has dropped to zero. At the start of the race, speed is low but acceleration high.

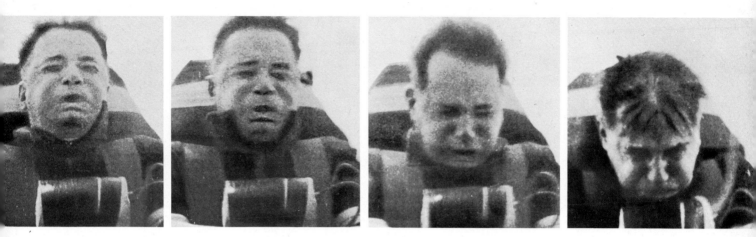

RATE OF CHANGE

A Way to Measure
Speeding Up
and Slowing Down

"Every shape that's born," the Roman poet Ovid wrote, "bears in its womb the seeds of change." Among the many kinds of change in today's high-geared world, one of the most familiar is acceleration, which is vividly illustrated in the distorted features of the passenger on the rocket sled above, and in the tensed muscles of runners at left, springing forward in a hundred-meter dash.

The exact acceleration—or the "rate of change of speed"—at any one of the moments shown above can be determined by depicting the entire ride in graph form.

When such a graph is drawn, as in the case of the boy's growth below, certain information is reflected in the curve: its unevenness, for example, reflects an uneven rate of growth from year to year. The rate of growth at any given point can be determined by drawing a line tangent to the curve—i.e., touching it at only one point. The slope of the tangent line measures the precise rate of growth at the point where it touches. If the slant of the tangent is steep, the rate of growth is rapid; if the tangent is horizontal, no growth is taking place at that point on the curve.

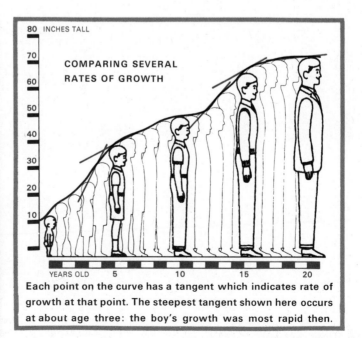

COMPARING SEVERAL
RATES OF GROWTH

80 INCHES TALL
70
60
50
40
30
20
10

YEARS OLD   5   10   15   20

Each point on the curve has a tangent which indicates rate of growth at that point. The steepest tangent shown here occurs at about age three: the boy's growth was most rapid then.

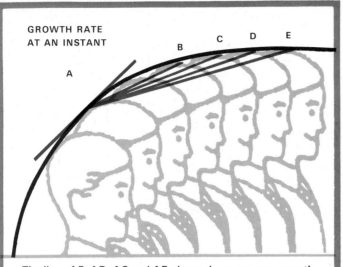

GROWTH RATE
AT AN INSTANT

The lines AE, AD, AC and AB above show average growth rates for successively smaller periods of time. But for the instant A, the growth rate is shown by the tangent at A.

CONVERGENCE

Using a Shrinking Ruler to Measure the Unmeasurable

A fundamental concept of calculus is "convergence to a limit"—the idea that an unknown value can be measured by "closing in" through approximations that are made finer and finer until they are refined, in effect, to a precise value. The tracks converging on the horizon at left suggest this method: although they never meet in fact, they appear to get so close to a point that for all practical purposes they can be said to join at that point.

Similarly, on the opposite page the images of the ever-smaller boy never actually shrink to a point. However, they do converge on such a small area that it is *considered* a point.

The drawing at top left illustrates how, in measuring a boy's growth rate over a span of time, the span can be shrunk until the measurement gives the growth rate—shown as a tangent—at a single instant.

Probably the best-known example of convergence is the 206-figure decimal expansion at the top of the page. This is a value of pi—the ratio of any circle's circumference to its diameter—and although it has been carried elsewhere to more places, no one has ever reached the end. But by extending the decimal as far as he wants, a mathematician can get as near to the true value of pi as he desires.

A "MEETING" OF THE TRACKS
Two tracks stretching endlessly across a prairie *(left)* never actually approach each other, but in perspective they draw closer until they appear to the eye to meet at the horizon. This concept of convergence at a point is used in calculus to give definite values to unmeasurable quantities.

AN ENDLESS TUNNEL OF MIRRORS
In this mirror trick a boy is photographed in one mirror while holding another, so that his image is reflected over and over ad infinitum. Each of the converging reflections is half the size of the one before; all together, if stacked vertically, they would be twice as high as the tallest boy.

821480865132823066470938446095505822317253594081284811174502841027019385211055596446229489549303819644288I

INTEGRATION

Finding Totals
by Stuffing Curves
with Rectangles

When some physical rate of change is graphed, the area under the curve has a special meaning: it represents the total of whatever value the curve represents. Thus, in the graph below of a salesman's earning rate, the area under the curve is his annual income. The technique by which the area under a curve is determined is called integration. There is no algebraic method for finding the area of such an odd-shaped figure, but calculus finds its precise area by filling it with rectangles of known area. These never completely fill the area under a curve, but the method of integration is to narrow the rectangles until the area they do not fill approaches zero. Then their total area is said to equal that under the curve.

A YEAR'S INCOME BY DOLLARS AND DIMES

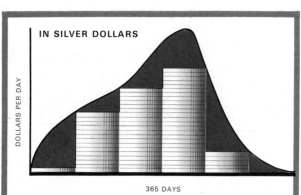

In this graph of a salesman's rate of earnings, the area under the curve is filled with dollars to indicate his yearly gross; a large error (the area shown in color) remains.

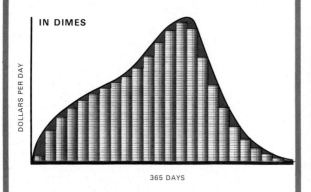

When the same area is filled with dimes rather than dollars, the error almost disappears. By using ever greater numbers of tinier coins, the total area is found exactly.

Nearly rectangular windows fill the area under the curving roof of M.I.T.

124

Kresge Auditorium in Cambridge, Massachusetts, architecturally illustrating the technique by which calculus finds the area under a curve.

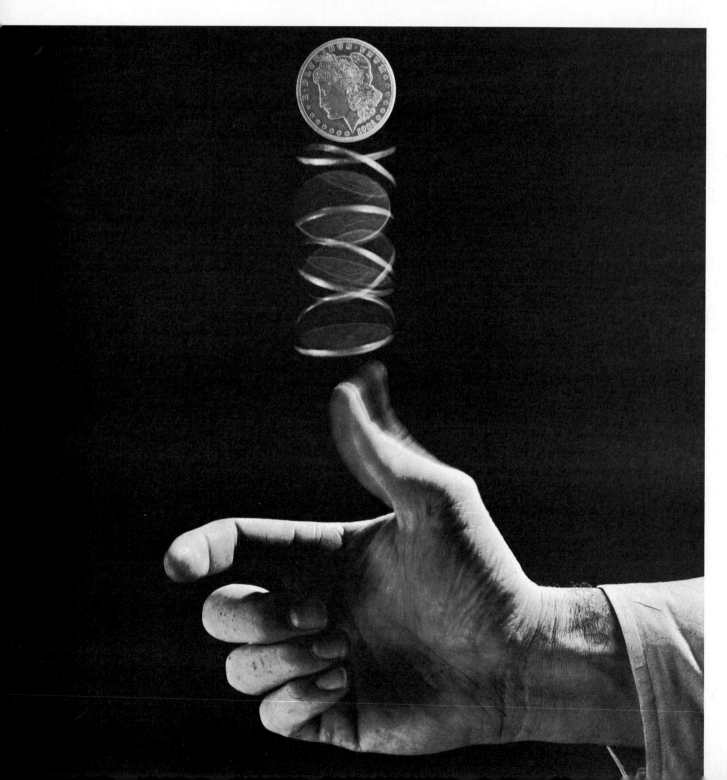

6

Figuring the Odds in an Uncertain World

BEYOND the certainties of death and taxes, few aspects of our lives elude the touch of chance. An unpredictable grouping of genes determines our physical make-up. An unplanned encounter may decide our choice of a mate or a job. An inadvertent misstep may land us in a hospital, a random pick of a sweepstakes winner may land us in a new income bracket. To all men, as long since noted in Ecclesiastes, "time and chance happeneth."

Unable to control chance, we do the next best: we try to evaluate the likelihood of the occurrence of a particular event. We pepper our talk with the adverbs of contingency: "usually . . . probably . . . perhaps." Every time we contemplate an event that is not yet accomplished fact, or whose outcome is beyond our influence, we automatically make an estimate of chance.

Gauging likelihoods has been a human preoccupation since time immemorial. Since the mid-17th Century it has also been a serious pursuit of the mathematician. Out of his researches into the subject has come an entire specialty of his profession—the mathematics of probability—and a way of computing chances which is much sharper than a layman's guesses. To the mathematician, probability is a percentage: the frequency with which one phenomenon takes place in relation to possible alternatives. When combined, the probabilities of particular events can be used to evaluate the chances of chains of events. To deal with such combinations, certain basic rules have been formulated; it is these rules which have come to be known as the laws of chance.

Many of the surest pronouncements of modern science are, in effect, hedged bets based on the laws of chance. But until about 50 years ago these laws were invoked almost apologetically. Mathematical theorists of the 18th and 19th Centuries reasoned that Newton's calculus, because it so successfully analyzed change and movement, could ultimately serve to reveal the future of any or all events with absolute precision. And so they held fast, for the most part, to a philosophy of "mechanistic determinism." The 18th Century French mathematician Pierre Simon de Laplace—who perfected Newtonian analysis of the solar system in a great work entitled *Mécanique céleste (Mechanics of the Heavens)* —wrote: "Given for one instant an intelligence which could comprehend all the forces by which nature is animated and . . . sufficiently vast to submit these data to analysis—it would embrace in the same formula the movements of the greatest bodies of the universe and those of the lightest atom: for it, nothing would be uncertain and the future as the past, would be present to its eyes."

Scientists today do not expect to acquire the instant understanding Laplace dreamed of. The ineffable smallness of the particles revealed by atom smashers and the ineffable largeness of the universe revealed

HEADS OR TAILS PROBABILITY
Tossing a coin is an exercise in probability theory which everyone has tried: calling either heads or tails is a fair bet because the chance of either result is one half. No one expects a coin to fall heads once in every two tosses, but in a large number of tosses the results tend to even out. For a coin to fall heads 50 consecutive times it would take a million men tossing coins 10 times a minute and 40 hours a week—and then it would happen only once every nine centuries!

by 20th Century telescopes have convinced them that they will never have at their fingertips "all the forces by which nature is animated" and —what is a great relief—that they will never be obliged "to submit these data to analysis." Even if this were possible, the calculations would be endless. And so modern analysts have turned, instead, to making prognostications based on the mathematics of probability.

Individually, the tiniest units in nature move about in a random fashion that apparently is not predictable. But they act in such great numbers that their collective behavior is thoroughly predictable—and with a known accuracy, a known chance of error, that is evaluated by probability. A population of trillions of gas molecules in a jar and a population of millions of Americans behind the wheel are predictable in the same way. It is impossible to foresee that molecule A will bump into molecule B or that driver X will crash into driver Y. It is, however, possible to say *about* how many molecules will collide in a second or *about* how many drivers in a month. And the forecast will be exact enough to let the scientist reach a useful conclusion or to let an insurance company establish its rates.

A start on the seamy side

In serving science and business, the mathematics of probability has attained a status far above its origins, which were slightly on the seamy side. Probability theory was inspired by the inquiries of gamblers seeking some inside information to help them win at cards and dice. Those raffish Renaissance algebraists, Tartaglia and Cardano, both came up with shrewd analyses of gambling problems. But their work—too gamy, perhaps, for mathematicians, and too mathematical for gamblers—was largely forgotten. Probability as we know it today was launched, instead, by a trio of Frenchmen in the mid-17th Century: a high-living nobleman, the Chevalier de Méré, and two spare-time mathematicians, Blaise Pascal and Pierre de Fermat.

Pascal's major interests were philosophy and religion. Another enthusiasm was "projective" geometry—a geometry dealing with the perspective problems of drawing and with the shadow forms which geometric shapes, held at various angles, will cast when thrown upon a screen. Fermat was a jurist by profession. As mentioned earlier, he created parts of analytic geometry independently of Descartes, but he is mainly remembered as one of the leading number theorists of all time, a reputation which he gained by moonlighting on quiet evenings at home after sessions in the local parliament.

In 1651 or 1652 De Méré and Pascal found themselves together on a trip to the town of Poitou. Searching about for a mutually interesting topic of conversation with which to lighten the journey, the worldly

A SPARED HEAD
Pierre Simon de Laplace (1749-1827) used calculus both to explore celestial mechanics and to advance probability theory—which he called "common sense reduced to calculus." He started out teaching mathematics at the Military School of Paris, where Napoleon was one of the students. In the Revolution, his head was spared so that he could calculate trajectories for the artillery.

De Méré presented the spiritual Pascal with a mathematical problem which had fascinated sporting bloods since the Middle Ages: how to split the pot in a dice game that has to be discontinued. Pascal pondered the problem for a couple of years and in 1654 relayed it to Fermat.

In the celebrated correspondence which ensued over De Méré's poser, Pascal and Fermat began by agreeing that in a discontinued dice game the stakes on the table should be divided according to the prospects each player has of winning. Let us suppose, for instance, that De Méré and one of his cronies were actually playing a dice game of those times. Each player has bet 32 pistoles (the equivalent of about $176 in gold value today) that his chosen number will turn up three times on a die before the other player's number has done so. After the game has been under way for a while, De Méré's number, 6, has turned up twice; his opponent's 4 has turned up only once. At this point De Méré receives a sudden summons to an audience with the young King Louis XIV. How should the players split the 64 pistoles on the table? De Méré's friend could contend that since his chances of getting two lucky throws are half as good as De Méré's chances of getting one lucky throw, he is entitled to half as much of the pot as De Méré is: $21\frac{1}{3}$ pistoles to De Méré's $42\frac{2}{3}$. De Méré, on the other hand, could contend that on the next throw of the die the worst that could happen to him would be to lose his advantage, in which case the game would be even and he would be entitled to an even-steven cut of 32 pistoles. If, however, his next throw were lucky, he would win the original bet and pick up all 64 pistoles. De Méré argues, therefore, that even before the throw he is entitled to the 32 pistoles he is sure of, plus 16 more he is half-sure of. And he is right: Pascal and Fermat so decided early in their correspondence.

Out of the researches of Pascal and Fermat into various gambling situations has evolved the modern theory of probability—the laws of chance. The idea that chance is governed by laws may seem unconvincing to anyone persuaded of the rule of Lady Luck. But actually the laws of chance do not preclude the possibility that an individual will enjoy a stroke of luck. Nor do they deny the value of playing hunches. They begin to act as laws only when many instances are involved—many throws of the dice, many deals of the cards, many car collisions, many lifetimes. This aspect of probability is known as the *law of large numbers*.

The same law gives an individual only a remote chance of being consistently lucky—of consistently doing much better than a probability prediction would warrant. On the other hand, a long run of good luck does not decrease the chance that an individual will again be lucky on any one occasion; a salesman who flies thousands of miles a year without accident does not incur a greater risk of crashing each new time he boards a plane. Runways and radar have no memory, and his chances of

A BOOK OF RANDOM NUMBERS
Random numbers are used in the research technique of random sampling. Humans are too full of associations to think up truly random numbers—no one would pick three 4s in a row but such a sequence might be a random series—so the RAND Corporation used an electronic roulette wheel to prepare the million-digit book of random number tables above. Part of a page is shown below.

06800	31827	80191	43585	20270	74558	48961	90052	02750	82718	27982
06801	92204	68347	84735	32061	47876	42152	89344	82877	44440	61944
06802	72608	47319	85449	66261	38104	76120	66105	86843	17467	79969
06803	71181	34112	21904	22894	46802	68360	67676	37401	50290	46941
06804	30238	58381	06203	10840	07664	84061	78870	19046	94038	74214
06805	97806	63153	46986	88540	26772	51091	60122	13542	29098	02527
06806	68901	15231	70325	54459	74210	33550	67053	03497	00764	59007
06807	51517	35148	82482	85693	34742	79244	54316	59097	05238	71302
06808	96035	69002	34342	01936	91700	87950	36445	27181	94249	35572
06809	40704	12590	78982	10013	72214	98454	63763	75478	24327	74597
06810	99130	52082	16513	04318	44844	62677	52651	92644	60732	82781
06811	71335	76694	81253	49676	62672	77020	33251	77045	66312	20038
06812	13116	26616	14165	91983	19943	51068	33249	54613	76240	99180
06813	97727	69794	70411	30598	83133	74098	05019	92651	23968	39257
06814	55499	59891	93900	73882	25113	59388	43088	23301	32577	52791

surviving a specific flight remain as good the 3,000th time as the first.

The law of large numbers accounts for most of the practical uses of probability today. Because of it, the probable accuracy of any forecast increases with the number of cases covered—the number of molecules in a jarful of gas or the number of accident insurance policies written. This is one reason why premiums run much higher on individual policies custom-tailored to cover a particular risk than on ordinary policies which can be spread out over large numbers of different cases. For instance, an insurance actuary may look up the weather records and find that on an average April day in Mexico City the chances of rain are less than two out of a hundred. But if a Mexican millionaire wishes to insure his daughter's outdoor wedding reception against rain, the insurance company will give him not 50-to-1 odds but only about 10-to-1 odds. That is, in order to collect for all the hors d'oeuvres and flowers that might be wasted if it rained, he would have to pay about a tenth as much for the insurance as these items cost him. On the other hand, if a driver bets an insurance company $100 that his car will not cause $300,000 worth of public damage in a year, he will be given much better odds. He will have to pay only slightly more than his share of all the damage that he and many thousands of drivers like him will do collectively.

Chicken tracks and children

The mathematics of probability legislates over many other facets of modern life besides insurance. It helps the atomic researcher interpret the chicken tracks left on film by atomic particles shot from cyclotrons. It helps the rocket expert decide what safety factors should be built into costly missile systems. It helps to rate our children on intelligence tests, to make possible pre-election-day pollster predictions, and to spot-check merchandise as it rolls from our production lines.

Basically, two laws underlie probability: a *both-and* law, to calculate the probability of two events both happening, and an *either-or* law, to calculate the probability of one or the other of two events happening. The both-and law states that the chance of two independent events both happening is equal to the probability of one happening multiplied by the probability of the other happening. For instance, the chance of turning up heads on one flip of a coin is 1/2. The chance of turning up heads on both the first and second flip is $1/2 \times 1/2$, or only 1/4. The either-or law states that the chance of either one or the other of two mutually exclusive possibilities coming true equals the sum—the addition—of the separate chances of each coming true individually. For instance, the chance of turning up either heads or tails on a flip of the coin is equal to the chance of throwing heads plus the chance of throwing tails: $1/2 + 1/2 = 1$. In the vocabulary of probability, the 1 represents

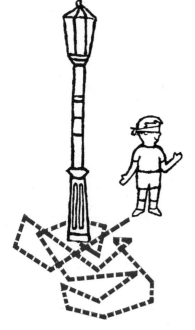

TAKING A RANDOM WALK
A blindfolded boy who walks away from a lamppost, changing direction now and then according to whim, moves in a wholly irregular fashion *(above)*. But the mathematical "law of disorder" predicts that as long as he keeps walking he will keep returning to the lamppost. This example illustrates the "random walk" principle of modern physics—once brilliantly employed to describe the movement of tiny particles suspended in a liquid by a 26-year-old physicist named Albert Einstein.

certainty—something that will come up once in every single trial.

Since events are frequently related—rather than independent or mutually exclusive—the both-and and either-or laws of probability carry important riders. The both-and law of two events is modified if the occurrence of the first event affects the chances of the second. For instance, the probability of drawing one of the 13 hearts in a 52-card deck is 13/52, or simply 1/4. But the chance of getting a heart on both the first and second draw from a deck is not 13/52 × 13/52. After one heart has been drawn and there are only 12 hearts and 51 cards left to choose from, the probability that a heart will turn up has decreased from 13/52 to 12/51. As a result, the both-and chances of drawing two hearts in a row have been reduced to 13/52 × 12/51. This modification of the both-and law is called the *law of conditional probability*.

A similar proviso attaches to the either-or law. If two events are not mutually exclusive, the combined chances of either one or the other coming to pass are equal to the sum of their separate chances minus the chance of their both occurring together. For instance, the Chevalier de Méré's chances of throwing either a 2 or a 3 on one cast of a single 6-face die would be 1/6 + 1/6 because the two outcomes are mutually exclusive —he could not possibly throw both numbers on a single toss. By contrast, his chances of throwing a 2 on either one or the other of two tosses would not be mutually exclusive; he could throw a 2 on both casts. As a result, the either-or chance of a 2 showing up on one or the other toss would be 1/6 + 1/6 modified by subtracting 1/36 to represent the both-and probability of two 2s in a row.

One great difficulty in applying the laws of probability lies in determining all the possible ways in which an event can take place. In dice games the problem is only moderately hard. Each successive toss of one die, or each new die added to a set of dice being thrown together, multiplies the number of possibilities by six. For instance, if three dice are being thrown the total number of possibilities is three 6s multiplied together, or 216. All these possibilities are equally likely, but many are identical in the effects—that is, a 15 can turn up either as a 3, 6, 6, a 6, 3, 6 or a 6, 6, 3. The only difference between them is their order of appearance, and the different orders of appearance must be considered in evaluating the probabilities. Baldly speaking, a man who ends up in a hospital with a broken leg does not care whether he stumbled and was then run over by a car or was first hit by the car and then knocked over. But each sequence of events has its own separate probability of occurring, and that morning, if he had figured his chances of winding up in the hospital, he would have had to take both possible sequences into account.

As a labor-saving device mathematicians have worked out rules that will tell them at a glance how many separate orders or arrangements are

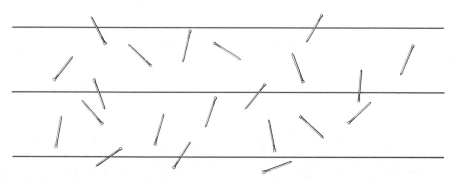

THE PROBABILITY OF A BROTHER HAVING A SISTER

If a man says, "Of my two children at least one is a boy," what is the probability that both are boys? The answer, oddly, is not "50-50." If the sex of the first-born is unknown, there are three possible sequences of children:

BOY, THEN BOY

BOY, THEN GIRL

GIRL, THEN BOY

Of these three possible arrangements, only one includes two boys: the probability that the other child is a boy is thus one in three, or 1/3. Had we known the man's *first* child was a boy, only the upper two figures above would be possible; and the probability of his having two boys would then be one out of two, or "50-50."

NAILING DOWN NEUTRONS
Throwing nails on a floor made of narrow boards illustrates a probability technique known as the Monte Carlo method, which was instrumental in developing the proper shielding for atomic reactors. By repeated throws of the nails it is possible to find just how often a nail will touch on a crack. Atomic scientists adapted the method—the only one which would work—to figure out the chances that a neutron produced by the fission of an atomic nucleus would be stopped or deflected by another nucleus in the shielding around it.

TAKING THE GUESSWORK OUT OF THE GRAB BAG

REACHING INTO THE BAG
If one reaches into the grab bag above, what is the probability of correctly predicting the order in which the three objects will be picked? This is a vest-pocket example of figuring out permutations and combinations:

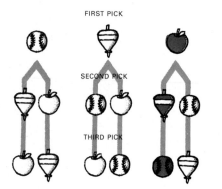

FIRST PICK

SECOND PICK

THIRD PICK

THE POSSIBLE ORDER OF PICKS
The three vertical columns in the above chart show the possible ways in which the grab bag could be emptied. In the column at left, the ball is picked first (the chances of this are one in three). Either the top or apple must be picked next (chances: one in two). If the top is picked, the third pick must yield the apple and vice versa (chances: one in one). The probability of guessing any one order of picks occurring is found by multiplying together the chances of each pick— i.e., 1/3 x 1/2 x 1/1—giving in this case, 1/6.

concealed in any one set of possibilities. A set of possibilities—the five possible cards in a poker hand, for instance—is known mathematically as a "combination." Each way in which the cards can be arranged, or each order in which they can be drawn, is known as a "permutation."

The laws of permutations and combinations by which probability theorists make life easier for themselves have been arrived at through pondering the orders or arrangements which can come out of a hat—any kind of lottery drawing, card dealing or picking from a grab bag (as at left). Suppose, for instance, that a bachelor is equally friendly with a redhead, a blonde and a brunette; suppose further that it is his chary nonmatrimonial policy to have one date with each girl in every set of three dates. How many permutations—dating orders—can he go through before repeating himself? On the first date of any set of three dates he has three possibilities. Having gone out with one of the girls, he has two choices left on the second evening of the set. After the second date he has only one choice left. In all, he has $3 \times 2 \times 1$ ways of arranging the sequence of his dates in a single set. And after six sets he is bound to start repeating himself because he has exhausted the possibilities.

A more common, if less intriguing, way in which the average citizen draws from a grab bag is at the card table. When the first card is dealt from a 52-card deck, there are 51 possibilities left; when the second card is dealt there are 50 possibilities left. *In toto* the number of ways 52 cards can be doled out or arranged is 52 times 51 times each lower number down to 1—an immense figure running to 68 digits. To save space mathematicians write it simply as a 52 followed by an exclamation point which they call "52-factorial." Five-factorial (5!) means $5 \times 4 \times 3 \times 2 \times 1$, or 120. Three-factorial (3!) means $3 \times 2 \times 1$, or 6.

The most happy bachelor

The player in a poker or bridge game is akin to our aforementioned bachelor—except that the bachelor is now leading a life of heavenly complexity. He knows 52 different girls and he chooses them in sets of five or 13. If he chooses in sets of five, the possibilities he faces before each choice are successively 52, 51, 50, 49 and 48, and his total possible dating orders number $52 \times 51 \times 50 \times 49 \times 48$ or 52!/(52-5)!—in all 311,875,200 different arrangements. If he chooses in sets of 13 the possible arrangements run to 52!/(52-13)!—which is an even more monstrous number.

In bridge or poker a player is not so much interested in the number of sequences by which he can draw a hand as in the number of possible hands which result. In poker he can draw five cards in 52!/(52-5)! ways but only 1/5!—or 1/120—of these ways have any significance for him because the rest are only other arrangements. Thus the total number of hands he can hold, disregarding the order in which he picks them, is

52!/(52-5)!(5!), or 2,598,960. In a similar way the total number of bridge hands is 52!/(52-13)!(13!)—in all 635,013,559,600. Generally speaking, the number of ways that r objects can be drawn out of a grab bag of n different objects, with no regard for their arrangement, is n!/r!(n-r)!.

Although probability still bears the marks of its sporting origins, it is not all dice games, cards, draws and tosses. In its more practical forms it is the major ingredient of the science of statistics. As applied through statistics, it gives the high-school student an idea of his future earning power if he goes through college instead of dropping out; it tells the bachelor approximately what chance he has of living as long as his married brother; it tells the brother approximately what chance he has of surviving his wife. In business, statistical probability is used to estimate the stock which a manufacturer should hold in reserve in his warehouse to meet unusual fluctuations in the demand for his products. In communications it reveals the number of connections—of combinations—which must be built into any telephone exchange or telegraph network. In the drug industry it indicates whether the reported effects of a new drug on experimental volunteers are statistically meaningful or merely the results of chance.

Between games of chance and most of these more complex and useful nongambling applications of probability, there is a fundamental difference. In gambling it may be difficult, but it is always possible, to enumerate all the possible outcomes of a risk: all the billions of hands that can come out of a deck of cards. In predicting the twists and turns of real life it is seldom possible to know in advance all the cards in the deck. In gambling probability, the mathematician is drawing chances out of a grab bag in which the kinds of pay-offs and their relative proportions are known in advance. In the statistical probability, the contents of the grab bag are unknown at the start; the problem is to take a well-judged experimental sampling from the bag and then assess the probability that it faithfully represents the entire contents of the bag.

One basic tool that mathematicians use in investigating unknown grab bags is the curve illustrated at right. This is the so-called "normal distribution" curve, which charts what is normal or average in a large number of test cases. One easy way to derive the curve is to throw a very large number of dice a very large number of times and then graph the number of times the combinations turn up against the values of the combinations themselves. The curve turns out to be a gently rounded bell-shaped one—the familiar I.Q., or grading, curve which crops up in innumerable disguises in almost every kind of statistical analysis.

The probability curve was first recognized and used by the mathematician Abraham de Moivre, a French Huguenot who had fled to England after the revocation of the Edict of Nantes in 1685. It was further

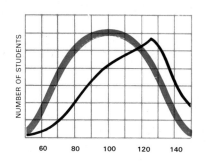

THE CURVE OF NORMALCY
The bell-shaped curve *(thick line above)* is the most common graph in probability theory. It describes all the variations in a group of events or quantities: the life span of light bulbs; the different sizes in leaves on a tree; the varying heights in a regiment of troops. If the sample is both random and large, the curve always appears bell-shaped. A random sample of I.Q.s in a big public school, for instance, yields a bell-shaped curve—showing that the great proportion of I.Q.s falls midway between the highest and lowest scores. Small, select samples on the other hand—e.g., I.Q.s at a school for the gifted—produce curves with their own special shape *(thin line above)*.

A BACHELOR IN TOWN
If a bachelor commuter has a 50 per cent chance of staying in town late to work, and also a 60 per cent chance of staying in town late on a date, it would appear that his over-all chances of staying in town late are 110 per cent! In fact, as the chart below indicates, he stays in town only 80 per cent of his evenings— 30 per cent of his evenings in town *(shaded area)* he both works late *and* then has a date. In probability theory, such events are described as not mutually exclusive.

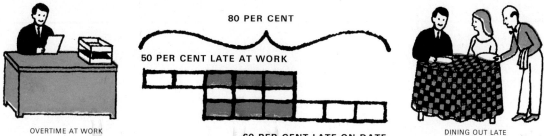

OVERTIME AT WORK

80 PER CENT

50 PER CENT LATE AT WORK

60 PER CENT LATE ON DATE

DINING OUT LATE

developed by the 19th Century's dean of mathematics, Carl Friedrich Gauss. To represent the curve Gauss wrote an equation which is of signal usefulness to the scientist because it is couched in terms of the factors which come into play in experimental situations. If, for instance, the scientist wishes to know what chance there is that the measurements he has made in an experiment are for some reason atypical and perhaps unreliable, Gauss's equation tells him what the chance is of the measurements being wrong by 1 per cent or by any other percentage. As a result the scientist knows "the probable limit of error" in his work and can act accordingly. Gauss's equation also helps statisticians judge whether a piece of information is meaningful or merely fortuitous.

Since the time of Gauss, probability experts have worked up other equations and other curves to fit various kinds of situations not covered by the normal-distribution curve. Such so-called "abnormal" situations would include, for instance, the chances of dialing a wrong number, or the chances of your home being hit during an air raid. The note of gambling persists in these sophisticated applications of probability, but it has been transposed upward to new octaves of usefulness and respectability. Today probability theory is no stranger to the high-school curriculum. And the hope is that youngsters who absorb it will become, not better card sharps, but better practitioners of the gambling arts of business, technology, science—or simply of the great gamble of life itself.

The Fascinating Game of Probability and Chance

For one brief moment when a coin is tossed into the air it assumes a state of unpredictability. No one can say which face will come up. Yet toss that coin a million times and it will, with increasingly minor variations, come up heads half the time and tails the rest. In essence, this is the basis of the theory of probability—a branch of mathematics which deals with likelihoods, predictabilities and chance. First enunciated 300 years ago, probability's earliest applications were in the field of gambling, to which it still has very strong ties *(opposite)*. But probability (like its handmaiden, statistics) has become an indispensable modern tool, predicting everything from life expectancies—in humans and light bulbs alike—to the positions of electrons. The Frenchman Pierre Simon de Laplace, preeminent in the field of probability, called it a science which began with play but evolved into "the most important object of human knowledge."

THE CHANCES AT BLACKJACK
Six players at a Las Vegas casino pit their luck against the bank in a game of blackjack, the object being to draw cards and get closest to 21 without going over. Seemingly a simple game, blackjack's probabilities approach the astronomical. However, one mathematician claims to have devised a system with the help of an electronic computer which will let him beat the house.

AN EMOTIONAL GAME OF 31
This 19th Century print depicts the entire gamut of human emotions—from elation to despair—among 10 gamblers at the moment when the winning card has been played. The game (and the name of the picture) is *Trente et Un,* or 31, a forerunner of the modern game of blackjack in which the winner was determined by whoever scored closest to 31 without going over.

A WHIMSICAL LOOK AT WHIST
The early 19th Century card-playing mania is satirized in this study by the famous British caricaturist George Cruikshank. Wearing elaborate wigs and feathered headdresses, the players here are intent upon hands of whist, an early form of bridge, in which trump is the last card dealt. Cruikshank's spoof is complete even to a kibitzer—the servant with the wineglasses.

Plotting
Percentages for an
Age-old Pastime

With simple changes in costume, the satirical gambling prints on these pages would be as timely today as they were when they were printed, 150 years ago. For games of chance are among the oldest and most universal of human diversions. The history of gambling is studded with dramatic episodes in which vast fortunes have ridden on the turn of a card or the roll of a die. The drama continues today: in the United States each year $15 billion changes hands legally—and perhaps an-

other $75 billion illegally—in gambling.

Despite high stakes, early gamblers played with little idea of the percentages for or against them. No adequate mathematical analysis of gambling was made until 1654, when two French mathematicians, Pierre de Fermat and Blaise Pascal, in a long exchange of letters, laid the foundations of probability theory. For the first time the vagaries of games of chance could be reduced to that measurable percentage of certainty, the odds.

THE GAMBLER'S FRIEND
Blaise Pascal, with Pierre de Fermat *(below)*, cofathered the theory of probability, prompted by the request of a gambler friend who wanted to know how to split the pot of an interrupted dice game.

A PART-TIME THEORIST
Pierre de Fermat, in addition to sharing honors for probability theory, contributed to number theory and gave differential calculus its impetus. A magistrate, Fermat was only a part-time mathematician.

ROYAL FLUSH — 649,739 to 1

STRAIGHT FLUSH — 72,192 to 1

FULL HOUSE — 693 to 1

FLUSH — 508 to 1

ONE PAIR — 1.37 to 1

STRAIGHT — 254 to 1

138

13 HIGHEST CARDS — 158,753,389,899 to 1

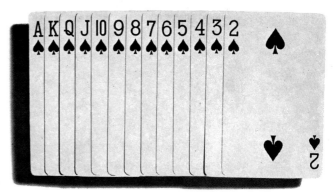

13-CARD SUIT — 158,753,389,899 to 1

The Mathematical Key to the Shuffled Deck

Building on Pascal and Fermat's framework, mathematicians proved that luck in cards is largely a matter of numbers—some of them astronomical. The total of different sequences possible in a 52-card deck is a figure 68 numerals long; if all the people on earth counted a million arrangements a second 24 hours a day, for 80 years, they could not count a billionth of a billionth of 1 per cent of the possibilities. The total number of five-card poker hands possible is 2,598,960. The number of 13-card bridge hands: 635,013,559,600. The odds for the sample poker hands (*opposite*) and bridge hands (*this page*) were computed by card expert Oswald Jacoby.

THE PERCENTAGES OF POLITICS
In the Renaissance cartoon at left, international politics is characterized as a game of chance, with all the participants, the rulers of Europe, dressed as playing cards. The fact is that card hands—if not politics—were vastly more predictable than these players of the period realized.

12-CARD SUIT, ACE HIGH — 367,484,698 to 1

NINE HONORS — 104 to 1

FOUR ACES — 378 to 1

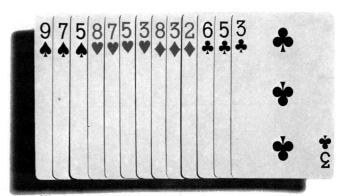

YARBOROUGH (NO FACE CARDS) — 1,827 to 1

An Immutable Law That No One Can Count On

The theory of probability deals only with the general—never the specific. For example, probability gives the young lady opposite one chance in 38 of winning on any given roulette number—but it makes no guarantee. She may win 10 times in a row; she may play 100 times and never win.

Besides refusing to be specific, probability is oblivious to setbacks. The arrangement of the dice below, a graphic display of what is possible with a single toss of two dice, shows that the chances of throwing "snake eyes" (double 1) are 1 in 36. But if a player should get snake eyes 100 times in a row, that would not lessen by one iota the 1 in 36 probability that his 101st turn will come up as a double 1. In this regard, probability has been likened to a kind of faith—unprovable on the one hand, immutable on the other.

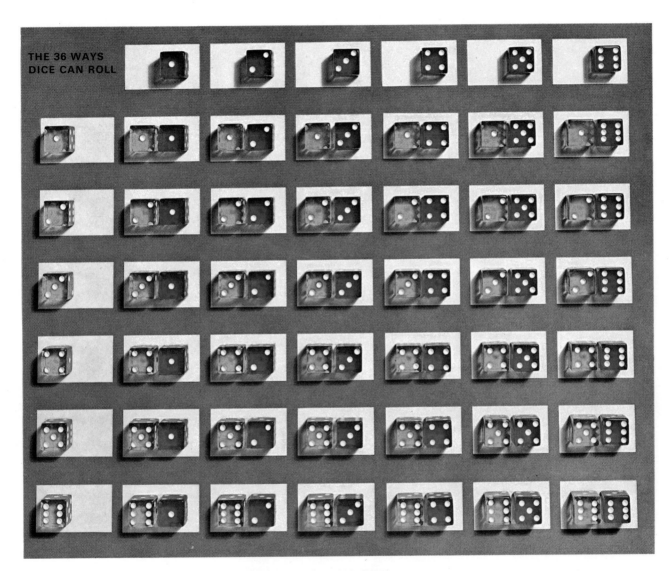

THE 36 WAYS DICE CAN ROLL

WEIGHING THE CUBES' ROLL
The paired dice above show all 36 possible combinations of a red die *(top row)* with a green die *(left)*. All arrangements to get a roll of 7 are shown diagonally, from lower left to upper right. Note that while there are only three possible number combinations that make 7 (6 and 1, 5 and 2, 4 and 3), there are six actual combinations of individual dice—a green 6 with a red 1, a red 6 with a green 1, and so on.

PLAYING A WHEEL'S ANGLES
A blond player lays her bet on the spin of a Las Vegas roulette wheel. Probability says she will lose—not necessarily on this turn, but in the long run. The house gives odds of 35 to 1. But actually there are 38 slots the ball may drop into (36 numbers, plus 0 and 00, visible at the far end of the board). In this way the house gains a theoretically unbeatable advantage in long-haul probability of $5^5/_{19}$ per cent.

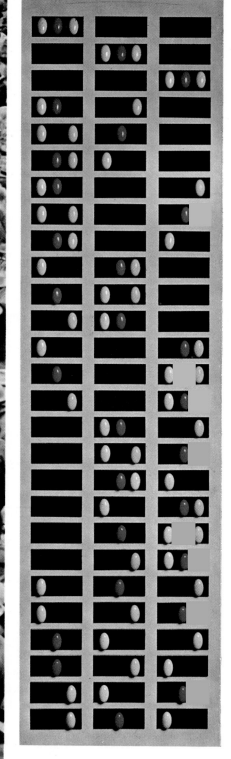

A MATCHING OF DATES

Of the 30 football spectators enclosed within the white frame above, the odds are better than two to one that at least two of them have birthdays on the same date. In a larger group, the chances for a shared birthday are even greater. Exactly how the odds change is demonstrated by the curve in the graph on the opposite page.

A MIXING OF BEANS

The figure above demonstrates how probability is calculated. Starting with the top row across, three colored "beans" have been arranged in all the possible ways they can be put into three boxes. To determine the probability that a given combination of beans and boxes will occur, the number of times in which such a combination appears in the model is divided by the total groupings possible, which is 27. Thus, the probability of all three of the beans turning up in a single box, for example, is 3/27—the number of times it happens in the model divided by 27.

COINCIDENTAL DEATHS

John Adams

James Monroe

Thomas Jefferson

COINCIDENTAL BIRTHS

James K. Polk

The Strange Influence of Probability on Births and Deaths

Although the coincidences of births and deaths shown on these pages may seem unusual, the fact is that they happen with mathematical regularity. Mathematicians aware of this have long made a parlor game of shared birthdays. The eminent mathematician Warren Weaver once explained the chance in favor of such double anniversaries to a dinner group of 22 high-ranking military men, and then started around the table to compare birthdays. To his dismay, he reached the last officer without turning up a single coincidence—but he was saved by the 24th person in the room. The waitress, who had been listening closely, suddenly announced that she had been born on the same day as one of the generals.

The reason these coincidences hold true is shown in the "beans in the boxes" model (*opposite*). There are just 27 ways to put three different beans in three different boxes. Similarly, there are just so many ways for 24 people (or any other number) to fit their birthdays into the 365 bins which are the days of the year.

Warren G. Harding

THE LIKELIHOOD OF SHARING A BIRTHDAY

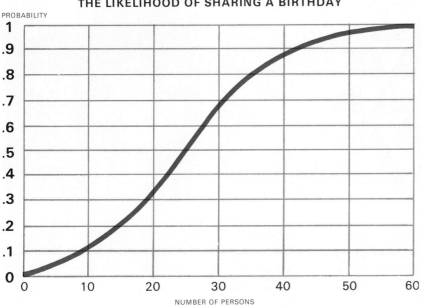

PROBABILITY

NUMBER OF PERSONS

THE CURVE OF COINCIDENCE
The chances of two persons in a group having the same birthday rise sharply as the group's size increases. Among 10 people, the probability is 1/10 (expressed on the graph as the decimal .1), among 25, about 5/10. Above 50, the chance approaches certainty (expressed as 1).

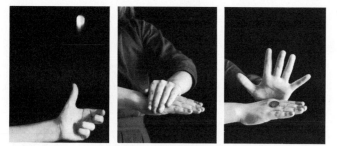

Heads or tails? Boy or girl? The chances always remain one in two.

The Fifty-Fifty Odds That Govern the Sex of a Baby

In the toss of a coin, the odds always remain 50-50—heads or tails. The same even chance applies to the birth of a child—boy or girl. Furthermore, in both cases the probabilities are unvarying, regardless of what has gone before. If a man has flipped 10 heads in a row, he cannot expect 10 tails to even things up. On the next toss, his chances remain 50-50. By the same token, the parents of all those girls on the opposite page (*lower right*) might feel that they are "due for a boy" after eight consecutive daughters, but probability still rates their chances at a fixed one in two.

However, these odds govern only one simple flip of a coin or the birth of a single child. Repeated tries may produce rare sequences, sometimes against enormous odds, like the families shown here. The chances of any parents having such amazing broods may be calculated using the technique indicated in the triangle below.

The Thomas V. Brennans of Oak Park, Illinois, an

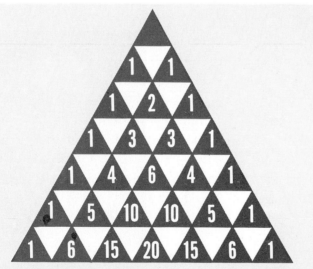

A TRIANGULAR TABLE OF ODDS
Pascal's triangle, named in honor of the 17th Century pioneer in the field of probability, is a ready reference for finding the odds governing combinations. Each number within the triangle is obtained by adding the two numbers immediately right and left above it. Computations are always made horizontally by rows: there are six rows shown, covering the chances ruling groups of one to six. The sum of the numbers in any row gives the total arrangements of combinations possible within that group. For example, to determine the probability of any given boy-girl combination in a family of six children, the numbers in the bottom row are first added, which gives a total of 64. The triangles at the ends of the row stand for the chances for the least likely combinations—that is, all boys or all girls: 1 in 64. The second triangles from the ends apply to the next most likely combination (five boys, one girl, or vice versa)—6 in 64. The center number—20—applies to three boys, three girls, for which the chances are 20 in 64.

A RUN OF 13 BOYS
Thirteen sons belonging to Mr. and Mrs. Emory Landon Harrison of Johnson City, Tennessee *(right)*, line up for a barefoot picture in New York City. Probability gives 1 chance in 8,192 for a family of 13 children being all males. Mrs. Harrison was 1955 "Honor Mother of the Year."

eir children make a rare grouping—five consecutive girls followed by six boys. The odds on this combination of 11 children are 1 in 2,048.

AN EIGHT-GIRL STREAK
Eight pretty daughters, born one after another to a single family, represent a 255-to-1 shot in the probabilities of eight-children families. While the chances for a ninth child being a boy are set at 50-50, the odds against an all-girl family of nine work out to be 511 to 1.

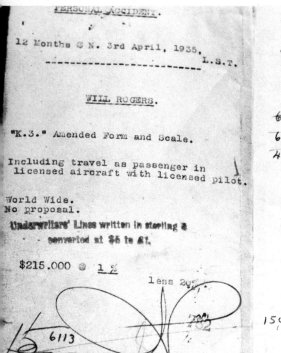

A CHALLENGE TO THE ODDS

A broker *(foreground)* bends over an underwriters' box at Lloyd's of London to discuss an insurance risk. A pioneer in the field, Lloyd's is famous for its willingness to underwrite unique risks for which adequate tables of probability are not available. These include damage to dancers' legs, rain-outs of public events and even the appearance of the Loch Ness monster.

THE PROBABILITY OF DEATH

A life insurance policy issued to the late Will Rogers shows a face value of $215,000, paid to his widow after Rogers' 1935 death in an Alaskan air crash. Note the typewritten addition *(left)* covering air travel. The price of such special coverage is high because the broad statistical basis for computing most insurance rates does not apply to such highly individual risks.

Mathematical Journey from Fact to Forecast

Probability and its helpmate statistics are, in a sense, like two people approaching the same house from opposite ends of the street. In probability the contributing factors are known, but a likely result can only be predicted. In statistics the end product is known but the causes are in doubt. A crap game, for example, is an illustration of probability: the two dice are capable of 36 different combinations *(page 141)*, and all of the probabilities are therefore available to anyone who can count.

These pages show three examples of the use of statistics. In life insurance, the actuary knows only that ultimately the policyholder will die. The factors governing the event as they apply to any given individual—when, why, how—are a mystery beyond prediction. The insurance expert must therefore draw up his actuarial tables entirely from death statistics, separating into categories such subdivisions

as age, sex and occupation. He thus starts with known statistics and from them works out the probabilities. As always in the case of probability, the greater the sampling the more accurate the resultant forecast will be.

The geneticist, working to unlock the secrets of heredity, including the complicated DNA molecule *(opposite)*, may approach his task in similar fashion. From a statistical sampling, covering such characteristics as height, weight, longevity and intelligence, the scientist can make accurate forecasts of the probable characteristics of unborn offspring.

Finally, there is the use of so-called random sampling, as with the fluorescent lamps at the right. In this process, the characteristics of a few individual items, chosen entirely by chance, are tested in order that probability then can be used to forecast with accuracy the characteristics of large numbers of similar items.

THE CHANCES OF INHERITANCE

A Seattle World's Fair visitor views models of the DNA molecule, determiner of genetic endowments. The model at left uses playing cards to depict the transmission of coded instructions. In terms of probability, such molecules can theoretically unite in $10^{2,400,000,000}$ ways. By comparison, the entire universe is estimated to contain only a scant 10^{76} atomic particles.

A SAMPLING OF LAMPS

A random sampling to test a production run of fluorescent lamps begins with selection of a few bulbs to represent the whole "population" in exhaustive tests. Random sampling is a common use of probability in industry; its reliability rests on picking the samples by pure chance. One expert suggested the tester take his sample whenever he rolled "boxcars" with dice.

A Logical Leap
into the
Wild Blue Yonder

ONCE A student has mastered arithmetic, geometry, algebra, analytic geometry and calculus, he is ready—as young grads love to tell freshmen—to begin studying mathematics. By this they mean the mathematics of the 19th Century, a period in which the entire subject of analysis took off into a wild blue yonder where the layman is lost and even the mathematician may grope. Before 1800 mathematicians by and large relied on their trained intuition and common sense, visualizing their thoughts in terms of realistic geometry or mechanics. After 1800, they began to rebuild mathematics on foundations stronger than mere common sense—on absolutely precise, persnickety logic. And by the end of the century mathematics was a wholly new edifice whose dreaming spires pierced the sky.

New legions of numbers sprang up in which the old ones we count by were included as a single rank. New functional relationships were framed which included the ordinary algebraic, trigonometric and logarithmic functions as mere by-products. Greek and Cartesian geometry became special cases in generalized geometries of n dimensions—geometries of surfaces and shapes which occupied more than the usual dimensions of height, width and depth, and which were therefore impossible to picture. Classical algebra became just one among many higher algebras—algebras in which whole paragraphs of traditional symbols were replaced by single characters manipulated according to strange new laws—that, for instance, $a \times b$ need not necessarily equal $b \times a$.

Learning of these wonders, any sensible person may feel that his worst suspicions about the woolliness of mathematics have been confirmed. In everyday conversation abstractness is often a cloak for vagueness, generality a mask for ignorance. But in mathematics the broadest statements can be the most useful of all. Today's mathematician is asked to solve an enormous variety of problems. The more comprehensive his classifications, the better the chance he has of pulling a sharp, precise equation for a particular job out of his mysterious hatful.

Mathematicians took the path of generality by necessity rather than choice. Throughout the 18th Century they had been busy exploring the practical realms of change and chance, following up the leads of great 17th Century innovators like Newton and Fermat. Switzerland's prolific Leonhard Euler—father of 13 children and author of 886 mathematical books and articles—created hosts of new uses for calculus as it applies to curves and surfaces. The French Academicians Joseph Louis Lagrange and Pierre Simon de Laplace were able, through calculus, to work out comprehensive theories of ordinary and celestial mechanics, thereby rearing a sturdy frame for modern engineering and astronomy.

Toward the beginning of the 19th Century mathematicians found that their hold on the abstractions they were dealing with was beginning

MATHEMATICAL BUBBLES
Soap bubbles drifting up from a blowpipe seem far removed from the cosmic questions which began to absorb mathematicians in the 19th Century, but the forces acting on them are among nature's most profound. They illustrate problems of maxima and minima—the bubbles always assume a shape with the least possible area—which were a central concern in the development of differential equations.

to slip. Questions were arising that defied the old common-sense treatment. Euler, for instance, had defined a functional relationship between two variables as "some curve described by freely leading the hand"—by which he meant simply a smooth curve. But did a "function" always have to be a smooth curve, or could the word also be applied to certain equations which represented groups of disconnected points? Could equations written in terms of more than three variables be thought of, perhaps, in terms of more than three dimensions—dimensions beyond the customary ones of height, width and depth? Could indefinitely long expressions like $x + x^2 + x^3 \ldots$ —what mathematicians call "infinite series"—be handled by the rules of arithmetic, as up to then, or were special caveats required to cope with their infiniteness?

Confronted by such conceptual difficulties, the mind began to boggle. Lagrange became so despondent that he gave up mathematics for a period of several years and, in a letter in 1781 to his friend and colleague Jean Baptiste D'Alembert, expressed the opinion that mathematics was delving too deep and in danger of being mined out. D'Alembert, in his turn, had no comfort for his disciples but the exhortation, "Keep going forward and faith will come to you."

At the very time that pessimism was settling over the mathematical camp, Carl Friedrich Gauss, the imperious German genius who was to dominate 19th Century mathematics, had just begun to display his prodigious bent for numbers. In 1779, while not yet three, the boy watched his foreman father tally up the payroll for the bricklaying crew under his charge. The father made a slip in his arithmetic and the son called attention to it. When the father went back over his figures, he found that his wunderkind had been right.

Gauss is perhaps the last genius who will ever make a single playground out of the subject of mathematics; during his long lifetime more new mathematics grew up around him, it is estimated, than in all centuries previously. Gauss gave direction to the new movement toward generality by imposing on it his own stern standard—a demand for absolutely rigorous thinking. In his own innovations, both analytical and geometrical, he started the ball rolling toward 20th Century relativity and atomic energy. For his researches into electricity he has been commemorated in the word "gauss," a unit of magnetism, and also in the naval term "degaussing," which means taking the magnetism out of a ship as an antimine measure. What is more, he and his associate, Wilhelm Weber, invented and built a workable telegraph and used it as an intercom system in 1833—some two years before Samuel F. B. Morse.

By his own account, Gauss thought out the rudiments of arithmetic before he could talk. At age 10, when his class at school was asked to add up all the numbers from 1 to 100, he instantaneously scribbled

A CITADEL OF GENIUS

Built during the Napoleonic Wars, the famous observatory of Germany's Göttingen University was the site of the profoundest mathematics of the 19th Century. Its first director was Carl Friedrich Gauss, greatest mathematician and astronomer of his time. A later director was Bernhard Riemann, Gauss's gifted student, who ventured into the labyrinth of non-Euclidean geometry and the curvature of space.

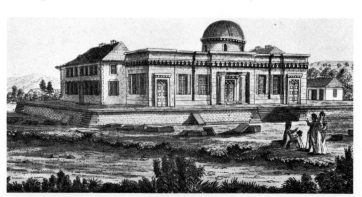

5050 on his slate and laid it down with the proud declaration, "There it lies." When the other students turned in their besmudged slates after considerable time and toil, no one except Gauss had the correct answer. Presumably Gauss had seen that each of the pairs of numbers—1 and 100, 2 and 99, 3 and 98, 4 and 97, and so on up to 50 and 51—adds up to 101, and that therefore the total of the 50 pairs must be 50×101.

A Mozart of mathematics

At 14 this mathematical Mozart came to the notice of Ferdinand, Duke of Brunswick, who thereafter subsidized the boy through preparatory school, university and the early stages of his career. Taking full advantage of his good fortune, Gauss devoured the classics and the logarithm tables with equal appetite and mastered Greek, Latin, French, English and Danish as well as geometry, algebra and calculus. When he was 19 he began to flood the pages of his notebooks with new mathematics of his own—new theorems in the abstruse realm of number theory, and radical schemes for generalizing the methods of geometry. He left many of his creations half-developed and never troubled to publish them. As a result, the full extent of his mental pioneering was not realized until his papers were published after his death. But such was his influence even in his own lifetime that other mathematicians were nagged by the feeling that whatever they were doing he had probably done earlier.

The squirrelish way Gauss had of hoarding his treasures is partly explained by his passion for perfection. "Few but ripe" was his motto—by which he meant that he did not want to clutter mathematics with anything that would prove a dead-end street or spend his efforts on any but the most promising of the ideas which tumbled through his mind. When the Paris Academy offered a prize to anyone who could prove or disprove a famous theorem propounded by Fermat, Gauss declined to enter the contest with a characteristic piece of bluntness that reveals the scope he always demanded of any mathematical effort. "I confess," he wrote, "that Fermat's Last Theorem as an isolated proposition has very little interest for me, because I could easily lay down a multitude of such propositions, which one could neither prove nor dispose of." Coming from anyone else, the remark would have seemed an idle boast. From Gauss it was a simple statement of fact—the kind that made him the wonder and despair of his colleagues.

Gauss is believed to have held back some of his ideas for fear that they would seem too unorthodox. He could see no a priori reason why space should be, as it were, laid out in straight lines—the way everyone since Euclid had assumed it to be. Why, indeed, should space not be curved? After all, a line measured in the one dimension of length can be curved. And a surface measured in the two dimensions of length and breadth can be curved. Why should not a space measured in the three dimensions of height, width and depth also be capable of curving? It was easy to entertain the possibility as an abstraction, but it was impossible to visualize the space that would result. So Gauss kept his own counsel and may even have doubted the sanity of the idea himself. In addition to being a champion of abstractness, he was a severely practical man.

Gauss helped pave the way to abstract higher algebra by his thoughts on a numerical breed known as the "complex number"—a number composed of an ordinary number plus some multiple of the imaginary unit, the square root of minus-one. He first grappled with these odd creatures of man's mind in his doctoral thesis of 1799, in which he proved the fundamental theorem of algebra: that every equation has as many solutions as its degree—a fact which mathematicians had been trying to make sure of for a century or more. In proving the theorem Gauss showed that all the solutions of every algebraic equation are, in fact, complex numbers—numbers either like $7 + 4\sqrt{-1}$ or like $3 + 0\sqrt{-1}$, which reduces simply to 3. Mathematicians customarily write the $\sqrt{-1}$ in such numbers as i, and any complex number as $a + bi$.

Later, in developing complex numbers, Gauss proposed a geometric way of looking at them which was to prove extremely fruitful. Ordinary numbers can all be thought of as lying along a single straight line, a continuous stream without gaps in it—what mathematicians call a "continuum." But a typical complex number, $a + bi$, has no place on the line of ordinary numbers. Gauss realized, however, that it could be thought of as labeling a point on a two-dimensional plane; that the a in this number could be thought of as a horizontal distance, and the b as a vertical distance, and that, in fact, the full $a + bi$ could determine the position of a point on the plane in exactly the way that the x and y of a Cartesian coordinate couplet determine a point on a graph. When two ordinary numbers are multiplied, the result is a jump along the straight line. When two complex numbers are multiplied, however, the result is a spectacular trapezelike swing within the two-dimensional plane.

The eccentric behavior of the complex numbers is important because it matches perfectly—and therefore serves as a literal translation of—the behavior of many quantities in nature, such as forces, velocities or accelerations, which act in definite directions. When two forces are exerted from different directions on the same point, for instance, their net effect is a third force with a new direction. Diagrammatically—as shown on the opposite page—the strength and direction of each of the two forces can be represented as the length and direction of a line segment. Each of these two line segments in turn can be represented by a complex number, and the two complex numbers added together will then represent the third force which arises from the combination of the first two.

The line segments that symbolize forces, velocities and the like are called "vectors," and are an essential tool of physics. The fact that they and complex numbers behave alike mathematically makes it possible to analyze complicated situations in which many forces are all acting at once—on the gyroscopic compass of a heaving ship, for instance.

Having helped to found vector analysis in two dimensions, Gauss went on, about 1819, to invent a class of numbers which would ultimately serve to represent forces, velocities and accelerations acting in more than two dimensions. These are the "hypercomplex numbers"—expressions like $a + bi + cj + dk$, in which the units i, j, and k, when multiplied together, produce minus-one. The most astonishing thing about these hypercomplex numbers is that they flout a basic rule of arithmetic previously thought inviolate. When multiplied together, the same two hypercomplex numbers may produce different results depending on the order in which they are taken; hypercomplex number a times hypercomplex number b does not always equal hypercomplex b times hypercomplex a.

The exotic and the heretic

To build an appropriate algebra for handling such numbers, mathematicians had to formulate new laws of arithmetic. Around 1840 Hermann Grassmann, a countryman of Gauss, faced up squarely to these appalling implications and worked out a consistent hypercomplex algebra—an algebra for which he invented several new processes of multiplication and in which vectors are handled in any number of dimensions whatever. In the decades following Grassmann's revolutionary work on vector analysis, which is still rocky reading for the mathematical avant-garde today, other types of exotic numbers were discovered that disobeyed other sacrosanct laws of arithmetic—that, for instance, $(ab)c$ must equal $a(bc)$. It was not long before different algebras, each with its own rules, symbols and equations, were as common as mushrooms.

Before the time of Gauss, mathematicians had treated i, the square root of minus-one, with gingerly respect and a certain outright incredulity. After complex numbers had been applied to forces and the like, i became a mathematical standby. Complex and hypercomplex numbers were increasingly incorporated into the equations of algebra and calculus. Mathematicians began to speak of "functions of complex variables," meaning relationships between variables with complex-number values. These they now used to pry, from certain stubborn differential equations, the answers to some highly practical problems in physics.

From the time Newton first employed them, differential equations have been a steady source of mathematical migraine and mathematical creativity. New equations demanding new solutions are always cropping up in scientific investigations. They arise out of many sorts of problems,

HOW TO HIT A BULL'S-EYE
Shooting at a target on a windy day is a problem illustrating one of Carl Gauss's complex realms of mathematics known as "vector analysis." In this diagram the velocity of the wind blowing from west to east is represented by the arrow, or "vector" V_1. The rifleman compensates by moving his gun slightly left of the target as represented by "vector" V_2. The bullet flies in a compromise pathway to the bull's-eye along line R.

153

but one category has been especially significant in the development of modern mathematical thought on cosmic and atomic questions. These are the so-called maximum-minimum problems, and they stem from what might be described as a tendency in nature to work with the greatest possible ease or the least possible effort. A ray of light reaching the eye from an object seen in a mirror has minimized its route by striking and leaving the mirror at equal angles. Two soap bubbles clinging together adjust so as to have the least possible surface area consistent with their content. As a perceptive 17th Century Italian physiologist, Giovanni Borelli, expressed it: "The perpetual law of nature is to act with a minimum of labor . . . avoiding, in so far as possible, inconveniences and prolixities." The laziness of nature—or "principle of least action" as it is called—applies to both static and dynamic equilibrium: the state of quiet following an uproar or the career of a satellite when it settles into orbit. A slack clothesline drooping in a catenary curve of minimum potential energy has reached a state of equilibrium with respect to gravity. In the same way the path of a light ray bouncing from a mirror can be thought of in terms of equilibrium—somewhat as if it were a necklace pulled into a V-shape by the weight of a pendant.

Calculus deals with all problems of equilibrium, and of maximizing and minimizing, by the same technique. Consider a salad bowl, for instance. The deepest point in the bowl is the point of minimum altitude or maximum depth. This is also the position of rest, the point of minimum energy, which a marble dropped into the bowl will finally come to when it stops rolling up and down and around. At this point the sides of the bowl cease to slope: the rate of change of the altitude is zero.

By letting rates of change—derivatives representing velocities or any other kind of change—equal zero, mathematicians seek to find the minimal or maximal routes nature takes in attaining its ends. The differential equations which result are the most important equations of practical science. When they have been integrated they turn into ordinary analytic formulas revealing the features behind the mask of change—variables like position, temperature, weight or electrical charge.

In the hands of an engineer, the principle of maximizing and minimizing through differential equations can be applied to specific situations even before they occur. In designing a bridge, for instance, he may imagine the bridge already built and then look for the state of equilibrium it will achieve in a 200-mile gale. If the mathematical equivalent of "let rate of change equal zero" turns out to be an equation without solution, then that means the bridge will find no resting point but will break in the gale. After putting more girders and cables into the bridge, the engineer can try again, mentally experimenting with wind and steel through the marvelous agency of differential equations.

SEEING ORDER IN CHAOS
Captured in Napoleon's disastrous Russian campaign of 1812, French mathematician Jean Victor Poncelet conquered the boredom of his prison camp by aligning a lot of disorganized non-Euclidean insights into a new branch of mathematics—projective geometry. Its aim: to study the properties of geometric shapes that stay unchanged when seen from a distance. One example: when the eye looks into a pyramid that contains a seemingly chaotic arrangement of colored cards *(below, left)*, it sees an orderly pattern *(below, right)* because of the angle at which "chaos" is projected through space to the eye.

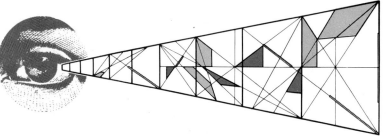
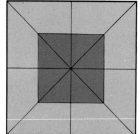

Probably the most celebrated differential equation ever devised is a "partial differential" equation which was posed by Laplace. It looks like this:

$$\frac{\partial^2 V}{\partial x^2} + \frac{\partial^2 V}{\partial y^2} + \frac{\partial^2 V}{\partial z^2} = 0.$$

Cryptic as it may appear, this equation has, in fact, been used to describe the stability of the solar system, the electric field around a charge of electricity, or the steady distribution of heat in a casserole under the broiler. Such are the nimble abstractions of mathematics.

No one preached or practiced the ideal of being versatile and general in mathematics more persuasively than Gauss. He first made himself famous, however, by a feat of purely practical computation. In 1801 the Italian astronomer Joseph Piazzi accidentally sighted the first of the minor planets, or asteroids. Now known as Ceres, this "clod of dirt," as Gauss called it, promptly escaped its discoverer and disappeared into the bright sections of the sky near the sun. The finding of the supposed new planet had caused a stir all over Europe. To have it so soon "mislaid" only added to the excitement. Unhappy astronomers faced the gargantuan task of calculating its whereabouts from the few fixes which had been taken on its position before it vanished. The calculations seemed impossibly difficult—to everyone, that is, but Gauss. Gauss loved to calculate as a soprano loves to hold high C, and Ceres gave him an unparalleled chance to surrender himself to the Babylonian joys of sheer arithmetic. Submerging into the logarithm tables he had memorized, he came up a few weeks later with a theoretical prediction of Ceres' entire orbit. When the little planet emerged on the other side of the sun, astronomers found it when and where Gauss had said they would.

After this triumph, Gauss was showered with honors from learned societies. In 1807 he accepted the directorship of the observatory at his own alma mater, the University of Göttingen in Germany. There—like some consultant oracle of antiquity—he presided over the mathematical community of Europe until his death some 50 years later. All the while, however, he never published anything about a queer geometrical idea which had fascinated him since his precocious youth. This was a thought akin to the concept of curved space. Gauss believed that new kinds of two-dimensional geometry might be developed from a strange new axiom that through a point that does not lie on a given line *more than one line* can be drawn parallel to that line. Such an axiom ran completely counter to common sense and Euclid—to the proposition that, through a point that does not lie on a given line, *one and only one line* can be drawn parallel to that line. Yet in his latter years Gauss saw his idea of non-Euclidean rules of parallelism applied to slices of curved space.

While Gauss anticipated the upheaval in geometry, others carried it

A RUSSIAN REVOLUTIONARY
Commemorating the 100th anniversary of the death of Nikolai Lobachevsky, this Russian stamp was issued in 1956. Lobachevsky was the first mathematician to publish a paper on non-Euclidean geometry—though Gauss, always reticent to publish, had worked out the new geometry in Germany about 35 years before. At the urging of Gauss, Lobachevsky was honored by the Royal Society of Göttingen.

out. In 1832 he got a letter from an old school friend, Farkas Bolyai, who wanted Gauss's opinion on the unorthodox ideas of his son Janos. By abandoning Euclid's postulate about parallelism, Janos had constructed a kind of non-Euclidean geometry which we now call "hyperbolic"—a geometry which can be used to describe the properties of figures on a trumpet-shaped surface, as opposed to Euclid's plane surface.

To the inquiry of the senior Bolyai, Gauss replied that young Janos had an excellent idea, but having pondered it himself for many years, he could not praise it without boasting. Janos Bolyai was understandably discouraged by this response and when he learned soon thereafter that the Russian mathematician Nikolai Lobachevsky had also had the idea of non-Euclidean geometry, he gave up mathematics for good.

Dimensions, fourth to umpteenth

The next young non-Euclidean innovator who came within Gauss's ken fared far better. This was Bernhard Riemann, who studied under Gauss at Göttingen. When he was due to give his trial lecture as a teacher, he submitted, according to custom, three possible subjects. Traditionally, the committee of professors who were to judge him chose one of the first two. But in Riemann's case, Gauss looked past the first two and asked that Riemann lecture on his third topic: the hypotheses which lie at the foundations of geometry. This topic was an unknown land, full of controversy and danger and non-Euclideanism. But after intensive work, Riemann delivered a lecture to the philosophical faculty of Göttingen in which, without using a single figure or formula, he propounded a radically new concept of the structure of geometric space. Probably no one understood it but Gauss. Gauss, however, was wildly enthusiastic—for Gauss—and Riemann was on his way to the worlds of the fourth, fifth, sixth and umpteenth dimensions.

Riemann's geometry of many dimensions, while it is hard to appreciate in visual terms, is easy enough to conceive of as an abstract possibility: as a simple progression from a line in the "one-space" of length, to a plane in the "two-space" of width and length, to a solid in the "three-space" of height, width and depth, and thence onward to spaces of more dimensions—for instance, of height, width, depth and time.

To loft his many-dimensional idea into orbit, Riemann—drawing in part on concepts developed by Gauss—generalized the properties of curves and surfaces so that they could apply to spaces. An appreciation of Riemann's epochal mental flight can be gained from a single detailed example concerning the all-important geometric property of "curvature." The curvature of a curve is the rate at which it curves. One measure of this rate is the size of the circle which nestles most snugly against the curve at a point. If the circle that fits the curve best at this point is very small, then the curve is bending fast and has a large amount of curvature at that point. If the circle that fits best is large, then the curve is bending slowly and has a small curvature.

The curvature of a surface is defined in much the same way as the curvature of a curve. At any one point on a surface the curvature does not need to be the same in all directions. A mountain, for instance, is likely to slope downward from its summit at varying rates depending on whether a climber descends by the gentle spur to the east or by the precipitous north face. The summit, however, can be thought of as the intersection point of an infinite number of curves which climb up one side and go down the other. At the summit one of these curves will have a greater curvature than all the rest and another will have a smaller curvature than all the rest. Gauss had found that the curvature at any point on a surface can be usefully defined as the product of the greatest and the least curvatures of all the lines which make up the surface at that point. This product is now called the "Gaussian curvature."

If a point on a surface lies in the equivalent of a mountain pass where the terrain east and west slopes upward, and the terrain north and south slopes downward, then the minimum downward curvature is an upward curvature—in other words, a negative downward curvature. By the definition of Gauss, the surface curvature at a point in the pass must be the product of a negative and a positive—therefore a negative. An example of a surface with negative curvature is the Western saddle. By contrast, a surface of positive curvature is one that is always rounding to meet itself, like an eggshell.

Gauss had also found that the curvature of a surface can be defined not only in terms of a person looking at the surface from the outside but equivalently in terms of measurements made within the paper-thin surface itself. Riemann extended this latter idea about surface curvature so as to give a precise mathematical description of space curvature. In doing this awesome abstract thinking, he relied heavily on a thoroughgoing analysis which he made on the reference networks of coordinate systems. In the Cartesian system the reference lines are straight lines on a plane. On the sphere of the earth the reference lines are those of latitude and longitude. On an egg they might be circles one way and ovals the other. In the reflector of a headlight they might be circles one way and parabolas the other.

Riemann realized that every surface or space in his higher geometry could be laid out according to many different networks of reference curves. And he found that equations written in terms of one coordinate system could often be vastly simplified when written in terms of a different set of reference curves. One of the handiest of the various sets of reference curves is made up of so-called "geodesics." A geodesic is sim-

A NEST OF SPACES
The radically new concepts of curved space projected by Bernhard Riemann are represented in the six curved surfaces below. Surfaces 1, 2 and 3 are curved in the same direction as the surface of a sphere and are said to have a "positive curvature." While the cylinder (4) curves in one of its dimensions, it is straight in the other and has "zero curvature" mathematically. Figures 5 and 6 exhibit the same "negative curvature" as the surface of a saddle. Riemann nested these spaces concentrically as shown directly below to indicate progression of curvature from positive, on the inside, to negative.

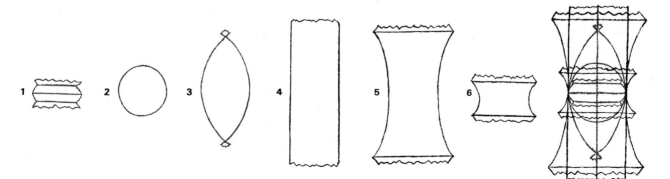

1   2   3   4   5   6

ply the path of shortest distance between two points. In a flat space a geodesic is a straight-line segment. On a sphere it is an arc of a great circle such as intercontinental jet planes follow over the earth. On an irregular lumpy surface or in a curved space, it may be almost any kind of curve. By manipulating elaborate differential equations to minimize distances, Riemann found that he could lay out geodesic networks of reference lines and follow the curvature for every kind of space from three dimensions on up to n dimensions.

In his daring geometry Riemann seemed to throw common sense out the window, but the art of analysis gained amazingly in dexterity. As in the marriage effected by Descartes between algebra and plane geometry, equations in many variables now found their geometric partners, and new symbols from the higher geometry became useful helpmeets in equations. And all the while the ideas at the bottom of the whole elaborate framework were simple ones like that of curvature—in effect, down-to-earth definitions which had long proved reliable in the tangible world of low dimensionality.

Gauss died in 1855, shortly after many-dimensional geometry was born. But the ideas that had incubated in his mind for 50-odd years were developed by Riemann and his successors, to become the practical methods which Einstein wielded another 50 years later when he gave modern man his present clues to the structure of the universe.

Three Who Changed Man's Concept of the Universe

The poised little fellow opposite, only eight when the picture was made, was already showing signs of becoming the mathematical genius who, as one of a great triumvirate, would someday alter man's view of the cosmos. As a 17-year-old, Carl Friedrich Gauss audaciously questioned certain rules of Euclid's geometry that generations of mathematicians had taken for granted, pointing out that many of them do not hold true on curved surfaces. Later he became fascinated by the complex problems of measurement on such surfaces. But it remained for Gauss's pupil Bernhard Riemann to shatter the boundaries of traditional geometry entirely, postulating curved spaces of three dimensions and finally fantastic spaces made up of four and more dimensions. Fifty years later, the physicist Albert Einstein brought the process to a stunning climax by borrowing these abstractions and, in his Theory of Relativity, using them to describe the real universe.

A BUDDING MATHEMATICIAN
Carl Friedrich Gauss is pictured in 1785 sampling a cherry while he was a student at St. Katharine School in Brunswick, Hanover, Germany. Always precocious, at the age of three he had corrected his father's payroll; now, in school, he so impressed his teachers that he was specially tutored in advanced mathematics and supplied with algebra texts like the books in this pen-and-ink drawing.

Classical "flat" space.

EUCLID'S COMMON-SENSE SPACE
This is Euclid's familiar uncurved plane, on which straight lines form the shortest paths, and triangles—whose angles always add up to 180°—can be moved without distortion. Gauss suggested that this plane was only a special case of a more general geometry that could just as well be applied to curved surfaces.

The Restless Mind of a Versatile Man of Mathematics

The many-sided genius Carl Friedrich Gauss had wide interests that included mathematics, astronomy and physics. He found the way to calculate the orbits of the asteroids, pioneered in electromagnetic theory and invented a telegraph. In mathematics he contributed profoundly to number theory, theory of functions, probability and statistics.

After conceiving of non-Euclidean geometry as a boy, Gauss did little to develop the idea. He pursued another line of research: the difficult job of measuring the curvature of surfaces. After a time he set that, too, aside. The two vital concepts lay dormant for years, waiting for the imaginative mathematician who would fuse them into a single powerful theory.

A SCIENTIST AND HIS TOOLS
Gauss, shown above as Christian Jensen portrayed him, in 1807 was appointed the first director of the Göttingen Observatory, which he helped make the most influential scientific and mathematical center of Europe. A display at Göttingen *(right)* shows articles Gauss used: a "Uranographia," or star atlas, an astronomical compass and a black velvet cap he always wore. Gregorian and binocular telescopes stand at rear.

MODELS OF THE HEAVENS

Gauss used these models at Göttingen to illustrate astronomical studies. In the foreground is a shape that the illustrious Kepler considered —and, according to the Latin inscription on it, ultimately rejected—while trying to work out his theory that the plan of the cosmos was expressible in elementary geometrical forms. The bristling shape at rear is a conceptual model of the solar system. Each ring of points represents the orbit of a different planet. Gauss achieved fame as an astronomer by devising a way to compute the orbit of the newly discovered asteroid Ceres.

A Disciple's Magical Blending of Doctrines

As he was growing old, Gauss made a discovery that would someday rank among his greatest achievements. This was the discovery of the brilliant mind of his pupil Bernhard Riemann.

For his introductory lecture before becoming an associate professor at Göttingen, the 28-year-old Riemann submitted three possible topics to Gauss. Gauss chose the third—an obscure subject that was not Riemann's favorite, having to do with the basic assumptions that underlie all geometry.

In the historic address that resulted, Riemann took the ideas of the youthful Gauss dealing with non-Euclidean geometry and joined them to some principles from Gauss's later work on measuring curved surfaces. From the combination of the two he formed a masterful system of "differential geometry" that revealed general ways for making measurements in a space of any curvature and any number of dimensions. As the old man Gauss listened to his pupil come to the end of this address, he is said to have uttered an exclamation of delighted comprehension. For the world at large, however, it would be another half century before the impact of Riemann's geometry would make itself felt.

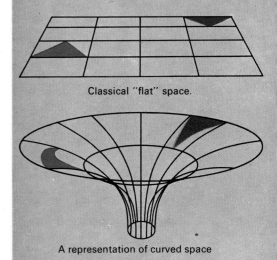

Classical "flat" space.

A representation of curved space

THE UNCONVENTIONAL SPACE OF RIEMANN
Riemann was concerned with curved spaces, whose characteristics are shown in the lower drawing. In such a space the shortest paths between points are curved lines, triangles are distorted when moved about and the sum of their angles—instead of always being 180°—would change as the triangles were shifted.

A SHORT BUT FRUITFUL LIFE
Bernhard Riemann, like his mentor, became director of the Göttingen Observatory, serving from 1859 to 1866, when he died of tuberculosis at 39. During his short career, he made major contributions in many fields, including topology, theory of functions and mathematical physics.

A SPHERE THAT BENDS INWARD
This model of a curved surface, reflecting a concept of Riemann, is called a pseudosphere—that is, a false sphere. Triangles on its surface can be moved without stretching, as they can on a sphere—but in the process the triangles are bent, which would not happen on a real sphere.

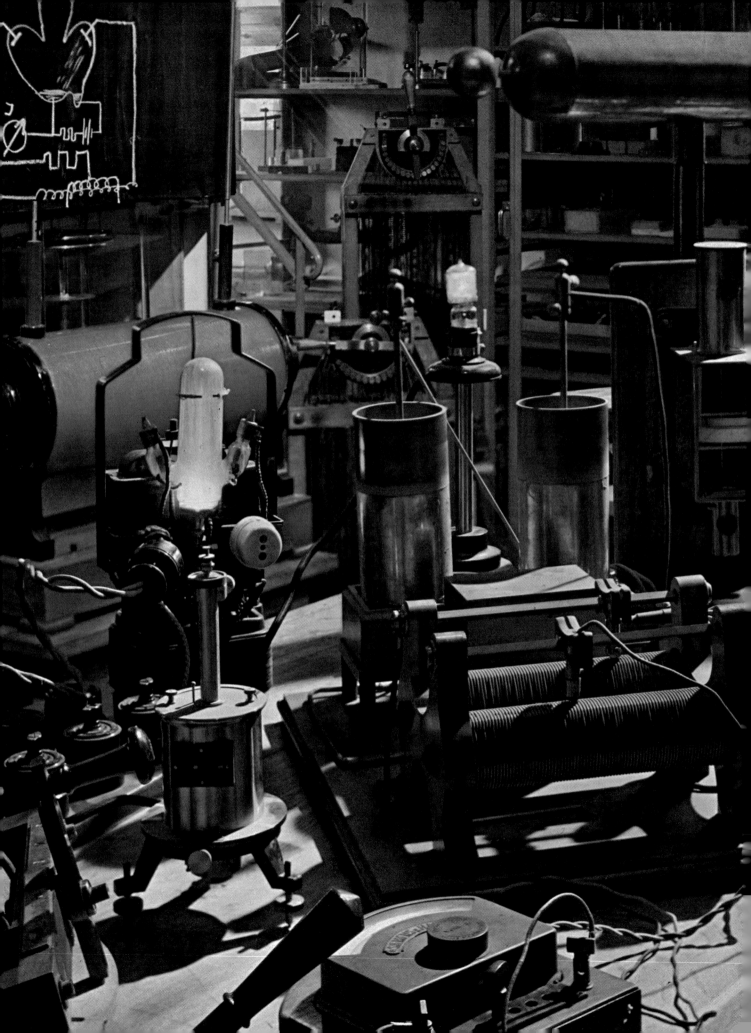

The Birth of an Idea That Shook the World

Each evening for several years near the turn of the century, an obscure clerk named Albert Einstein sat in a Swiss patent office puzzling over some unusual scientific observations—indications that the universe was not acting in precisely the way that Newton's long-accepted laws said it should. The speed of light, for example, appeared to be constant in all experimental observations, no matter how fast the light source or the observer moved with respect to the beam. To account for this, Einstein pieced out a strange theory called "Relativity," which said that time, length and weight are not absolutes, but vary according to speed.

Applying ideas of Gauss and Riemann, Einstein also suggested the existence of a curved universe of four dimensions—a cosmos in which, besides the three conventional dimensions of height, width and breadth, a fourth dimension of time was added, and in which the presence of matter accounted for the curvature. Even for scientists this was a difficult concept, but it fascinated them as a possible answer to hitherto unfathomable mysteries.

A GREAT MAN'S WORKSHOP
In this laboratory of the Polytechnic School in Zurich, Switzerland *(left)*, cluttered with old-fashioned apparatus for physics experiments, Einstein gained his early knowledge of some of the phenomena that he was to weld into his bold theories. Though born in Germany, he studied here between 1896 and 1899, planning to teach physics and mathematics to gain free time for his own research. But he was unable to find an opening in any Swiss school.

THE AUTHOR OF RELATIVITY
Shortly before his death in 1955, Einstein is shown on the porch of his Princeton, New Jersey, home. Here he defied age to work on his Unified Field Theory, an extension of Relativity.

THE BIRTHPLACE OF RELATIVITY
This is a view from Einstein's home in Bern, where, after his day's work at the Swiss Patent Office, he played Mozart on his violin for relaxation and worked out his Theory of Relativity.

Classical "flat" space

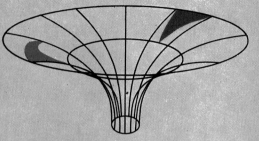

A representation of curved space

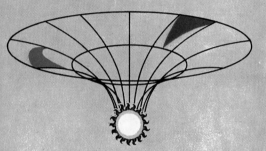

Curved space applied to the cosmos

THE COSMIC SPACE OF EINSTEIN
A celestial body such as a star (yellow ball) can be viewed as the center of a section of Riemann's curved space. According to Relativity, the star's mass creates the curvature, and it is this warpage of space rather than the pull of a body on others that causes the effects of gravity.

GETTING ENERGY FROM MATTER
The purple glow of the atomic reactor above and the H-bomb's fireball at right are the fruits of a Relativity equation. This equation, $E = mc^2$, states that matter and energy are equivalent. One can obtain energy (E) equal to the quantity of the matter (m) multiplied by the square of the fantastic speed of light (c): 186,000 miles per second. Theoretically, one pound of any kind of matter contains enough energy to propel the largest ocean liner on two Atlantic crossings.

Explosive Proof of Einstein's Mathematics

The power of mathematics has rarely been shown more effectively than through Relativity. Though mathematicians long ago accepted abstractions such as infinities or square roots of negative numbers, Relativity seemed to run counter both to everyday experience and to standard physics. Yet it pulled all the observed facts so neatly together that the scientists were intrigued. Then, as more and more evidence came in, their intrigue turned to conviction of Relativity's rightness.

For the layman, the most unforgettable demonstration was the one that confirmed the accuracy of a Relativity equation indicating matter and energy are forms of the same thing. The awesome evidence came with explosions like the one below.

But the parts of Relativity based on the mathematics of Gauss and Riemann have consequences even more radical to the scientist: they furnish a new picture of the whole universe. From these equations Einstein made certain physical predictions which scientists were soon verifying with amazing consistency. Light rays appear to bend; planets' orbits have strange quirks that classical physics cannot account for, exactly as Einstein predicted.

OUR DENTED SOLAR SYSTEM

A clay model shows how the sun (yellow) and the surrounding planets all create their own curved pockets in space, according to Einstein's theory. Einstein predicted that because of this warping, light rays passing near heavenly bodies would be bent—and scientists have verified this deflection. Much the same thing happens to a spaceship; its path wobbles through the "depressions" of the cosmos, just as if it were a golf ball rolling across an undulating green.

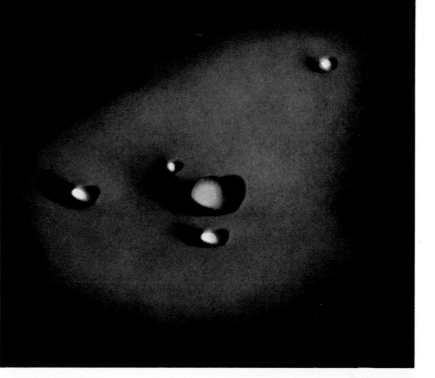

8

Mathematics Today: Deeds, Doubts, Dreams

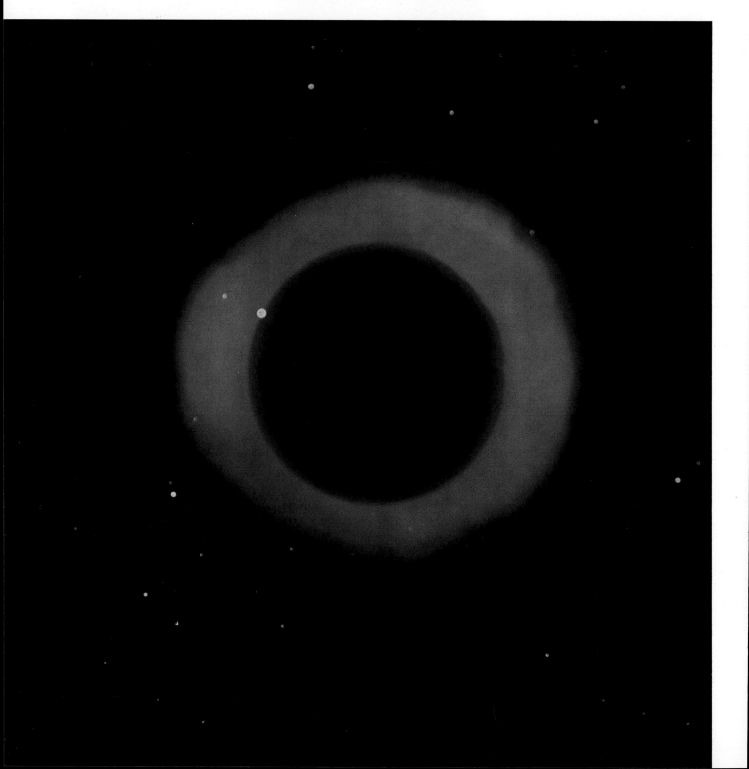

LIKE JACK'S beanstalk, mathematics in the 20th Century goes on growing without end. The number of mathematicians, 38,000 at last count, has increased several hundredfold since 1900. Huge enterprises like IBM, Bell Telephone and General Electric maintain grassy research centers—called "funny farms" by the disrespectful—where whole platoons of mathematicians are paid to do little else but think. The Pentagon abounds with mathematical Ph.D.s. Electronic computers—those minions of the mathematicians—now serve at many of the nerve centers of society: at the command centers of missile silos and battleships, at the Bureau of Internal Revenue, at the reservations desks of airlines, at the New York Stock Exchange.

Mathematics, in short, is in the thick of modern life. Never before has an ivory tower cast so long a shadow over the everyday world. At the same time, paradoxically, its initiates have not repented of their penchant for the abstract. They have made themselves at home in the wild blue yonder staked out by 19th Century mathematics. And there they now consort with abstractions of abstractions, with "covariants" and "contravariants," "transformation groups" and "transfinite numbers," "discontinuous deformations" and "topological spaces."

Such excursions into pure mathematical fancy, although they seem hopelessly impractical, have an odd way of running ahead of physical science, of supplying equations that fit the facts before science stumbles on facts that fit the equations. This has happened so many times—and also failed to happen so many times—that many mathematicians see themselves as formulators of possibilities rather than as discoverers of truth. The license imparted by this "art-for-art's-sake" outlook has resulted in a prodigal inventiveness. Like the hordes and horses of some fabulous khan, today's mathematicians have ridden off in all directions at once, conquering faster than they can send messages home.

Scholars who have tried to keep track of this rampaging expansion assure us that we are living in the Golden Age of mathematics; they estimate that almost as much new mathematics has been created in the last 60 years as in all previous centuries combined. Statistics bear them out. According to a recent tally of the reviews in *Mathematical Reviews*, the number of papers published by creative mathematicians doubled from 1940 to 1950, doubled again from 1950 to 1960, and increased by another 70 per cent in the next three years. Monsieur Bourbaki, the pseudonymous supersavant who represents the collective writing effort of a group of French intellectuals, has issued some 30 weighty volumes of an encyclopedia on the foundations of modern mathematics and has not yet gotten down to analytic geometry.

In both range and remoteness, modern mathematics defies easy description. In general, however, it has developed along two lines: on the

A THEORY'S STARRY PROOFS
The planetarium photograph opposite
symbolizes the first verification of
Einstein's General Theory of Relativity, a
20th Century achievement in physics based
on the brilliance of 19th Century mathematics.
During the eclipse of 1919, which is
re-created here, scientists discovered starlight
was being bent when it passed the sun,
as predicted by Relativity.

SYMBOLS FOR SENTENCES: BOOLEAN ALGEBRA

The English genius George Boole developed symbolic logic to clarify difficult Aristotelian logic. His system is used widely today as a tool to help sound reasoning. Boole's basic idea was that if the simple propositions of logic could be represented by precise symbols, the relations between two propositions could be read as precisely as an

algebraic equation—in fact, he created the branch of mathematics known as Boolean algebra. The chart below illustrates a simple Boolean system. The letters P and Q along the top row stand for the short sentences below them; the V and the small black square stand for the conjunctions—"or" and "and" respectively—by which the short sentences are combined. Reading in rows across the table, P and Q statements are true and false as indicated by the tinted key at the left. Whether a true P and a false Q, for example, "add up" to a true or false complete statement is shown by the true-false column in the center of each table. The table under the first sentence, "P or Q"—P V Q—shows that the sentence is always true unless both P and Q are false. The table under the second sentence, "P and Q" —P ■ Q—shows that the sentence is always false unless both P and Q are true. This chart is known as a "truth table" and, although the results in this case seem only common sense, such tables can help to resolve the most abstruse philosophic debates. Today, abstract Boolean algebra has practical uses in designing parts of telephone circuits and electronic computers—and even in arguing lawsuits.

one hand success and conquest—the ability to solve problems; on the other hand soul-searching and contemplation—an uncertainty as to the nature and aim of ultimate mathematical abstractions. Both these strands are woven into the many-splendored fabric of mathematics today.

On the contemplative side, two of the most notable developments are set theory and symbolic logic. Set theory, among other things, provides a new kind of arithmetic for dealing with infinity; symbolic logic is an attempt to reduce all human reasoning to a mathematical notation. Both set theory and symbolic logic are abetted by a third form of mathematics, group theory, which plays a unifying role in analysis and reveals unexpected similarities between different mathematical domains.

Among its major conquests, 20th Century mathematics counts two whole new kingdoms: game theory and topology. Game theory is the analysis of strategy, whether in the hot games of business or the cold games of war. Topology is the study of the properties of geometric shapes which do not change when the shapes themselves are stretched, twisted, scrunched up or turned inside out.

Of all the practical triumphs of mathematics, the most spectacular has been Relativity, which, in heralding our nuclear age, has irrevocably proved the awesome power that mathematics can wield over everyday life. Relativity's creator, Albert Einstein, who began to reform the universe as an obscure young patent clerk in Switzerland, became, in his shy, shaggy way, one of the great personalities of our time. As such he helped to bridge a widening gap between mathematics and the public.

The Theory of Relativity, Einstein's masterwork, is really two theories: Special Relativity and General Relativity, the former published in 1905, the latter in 1916. Both theories are based on the premise that all scientific measurements are relative to the reference frame of the beholder: that there is no fixed center in the cosmos for scientists to start from in measuring off distances and describing exactly where and when anything takes place in space.

In effect, Special Relativity is a rewrite of the equations of Newtonian mechanics to correct their inadequate descriptions of energy and of objects—distant galaxies or atomic particles—which move at nearly the speed of light, 186,000 miles per second. The portentous equation of nuclear power, $E = mc^2$ (which means that energy, E, in a piece of matter amounts to the mass, m, of the matter times the square of the enormous speed of light, c), came out of Special Relativity as a corollary.

General Relativity pursued the same theme as Special Relativity— but with a vengeance. In Special Relativity, Einstein had overhauled Newtonian laws so that they would apply to fast-moving bodies traveling with *steady* speeds along *straight* lines. In General Relativity he broadened his equations so that they would apply to bodies traveling

P	Q	P I'll Call You Tonight	V	Q I'll Call You Tomorrow	P I'll Call You Tonight	■	Q I'll Call You Tomorrow
		I'll Call You Tonight or Tomorrow			I'll Call You Tonight and Tomorrow		
T	T	He Calls Tonight	True	He Calls Tomorrow	He Calls Tonight	True	He Calls Tomorrow
F	T	He Does Not Call Tonight	True	He Calls Tomorrow	He Does Not Call Tonight	False	He Calls Tomorrow
T	F	He Calls Tonight	True	He Does Not Call Tomorrow	He Calls Tonight	False	He Does Not Call Tomorrow
F	F	He Does Not Call Tonight	False	He Does Not Call Tomorrow	He Does Not Call Tonight	False	He Does Not Call Tomorrow

with *changing* speeds along *curved* lines. These so-called "field equations" of General Relativity not only cover every possible state of motion but also describe the over-all behavior of our universe and other conceivable universes past, present or future. The reach of the equations—a few difficult symbols tantamount to entire books of philosophy—staggers the mind and beggars the imagination.

Einstein was able to achieve such formulas only because he adopted and adapted the totally hypothetical, seemingly useless ideas of Riemann about curved geometric space. According to Einstein the real space in which men walk and the stars pursue their courses is, in very truth, curved. Evidence that space is curved near the sun began to accumulate almost at once after the publication of General Relativity. In 1919 astronomers on eclipse-watching safaris to Brazil and West Africa found that beams of starlight passing close to the rim of the sun bend slightly and so make their parent stars seem slightly displaced in the sky. Not long afterward, astronomical findings concerning a creeping shift in the orbit of Mercury and a reddening of light from certain stars also confirmed Einstein's ideas of space curvature.

To work his wonders, Einstein arrayed the moving matter and energy of the cosmos within a mathematical framework of four dimensions: three for space and one for time. He included time because he had found in Special Relativity that time and space are inseparable—that the time at which an event occurs is not independent of the place at which it occurs. In Einstein's space-time "continuum," matter and gravity are manifestations of each other; matter can be thought of as an infusion of gravity, varying in strength from point to point like the electric potential around a charged metal plate. The concentrations in this gravitational aura, or "field," as it is called, are the particles of matter.

A cosmic pinball machine

It is the presence of gravity in the continuum that provides the curvature of space. The effect is somewhat akin to that created by the little magnets under the playing surface of some pinball machines. When the magnets are switched off, the surface acts like a flat inclined plane, but when they are turned on, the surface behaves as if it were full of hills and valleys which speed and slow the rolling balls on their wandering way. In Einstein's cosmic pinball machine, matter and its alter ego, energy, play the role of both marbles and magnets, shaping the space around them as they move.

(Mathematicians emphasize that descriptions like these must not be taken too literally. How treacherous they can be is illustrated by an anecdote told about Einstein and a Russian theorist who was dilating on Relativity in a lecture at which Einstein was present. In an attempt

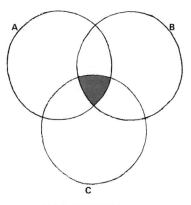

OVERLAPPING ANSWERS
In this "Venn diagram," developed by John Venn in 1880, the areas replace sets of things: circle A stands for "people who are French"; B for "people who are generals"; and C for "people who wear medals." Relationships between these sets of people can be read from the diagram. The colored area represents French generals who wear medals. Such illustrations of "set theory," a new branch of mathematics, are used today in teaching children *(Appendix, page 193).*

LOGIC IN WONDERLAND
Lewis Carroll was the pen name of the Oxford mathematician Charles Dodgson, author of *Alice's Adventures in Wonderland* and finest photographer of children in Victorian England. Though Dodgson signed his real name to only his "serious" mathematical works, mathematicians for decades have been intrigued by the rich skein of symbolic logic *(opposite)* that is woven into fantasies like *Alice* and *Through the Looking Glass*.

A TRAGIC PRODIGY
Evariste Galois, a fiery French teenager constantly failing exams and fighting teachers, was imprisoned for threatening the king's life and finally killed in a duel over a harlot. Though dead at the age of 20, he had already made his mark as one of the most original mathematicians who ever lived.

to simplify, the Russian compared one of his equations to "a cup and a saucer as they fly in space." At this point, the story goes, Einstein leaped to his feet protesting, and after a mystifying exchange of equations with the Russian stalked back to his seat. Crestfallen, the Russian concluded his presentation summarily. When he had finished, onlookers clustered around Einstein wanting to know what had happened. "This situation he was describing," said Einstein, "he said it was like a cup and saucer in space, but it was really like two cups and two saucers.")

In tackling questions of the cosmos—or indeed of the atom—abstract mathematics has been put to almost surrealistic usefulness. This in itself has been a source of delight to mathematicians, but also a source of dilemma. How go about creating more mathematics of the same scope? How judge the lines of analysis which will prove out in the future?

Mathematicians know no answer to this predicament. Some work by the creed "think concretely." Others invent for the sake of their art alone. By and large, the philosophical difference between the two schools has little effect on their actual working methods. Both seek to express their creations in the most general terms possible, to cover broad spectra of possible specific problems. And both try to keep slipshod definitions and faulty reasoning from stealing in among their abstractions—abstractions to which they cannot apply the usual tests of experience.

The way of a whatchamacallit

To explore the labyrinths where future giants of knowledge may crouch, modern mathematicians light their way by the set theory, group theory and symbolic logic mentioned earlier. Group and set theory are both used to compare the tools of different branches of mathematics and to make them as freely interchangeable as possible. A set is any collection of entities, whether whole numbers, nut-brown maidens or eggheads with horn-rimmed glasses. A group is a particular kind of set: of numbers, symbols, points, lines, movements, atoms, units of energy or undefined whatchamacallits. It is distinguished from just any old set by having to obey certain rules in regard to some operation like addition or multiplication. For instance, the offspring of any two members of the set, when they are combined by the operation, must remain in the set—the "4" produced by the wedding of "2" and "2" is also a whole number. Moreover, when several members of the set are combined by the operation, the way in which they are bracketed must not affect the result—for instance, $a(bc)$ must equal $(ab)c$.

Set theory was developed by the German mathematician Georg Cantor as a technique for "anatomizing the infinite." During the 19th Century there had been sustained attempts to define infinite processes like differentiation and integration in terms of simple arithmetic. The feeling was that if all processes and symbols could be so defined there would be less difficulty in reasoning accurately about them. As one mathematician, Leopold Kronecker, put it: "The whole numbers has the Dear God made. All else is man's work."

It was Cantor's triumph, in set theory, to distinguish different orders of infinity in different infinite sets. He compared infinite sets by pairing off their members, two by two, like the animals boarding Noah's ark or the teeth of a zipper being zipped up. By this seemingly simple method, he reached some astonishing conclusions. For instance, all the fractions can be matched off against the infinite set of all the whole numbers. The two infinite sets are thus "equal," yet the set of all fractions includes the set of all whole numbers by virtue of terms such as 2/1 or 6/2; in other words, though the two sets are equal, one contains the other as a "subset." By the same technique, Cantor found that other infinite sets—all the points on a line segment, for instance—cannot be matched off against the whole numbers. In short, they cannot be counted; the points are infinitely more infinite than the whole numbers. Cantor found other orders of infinity—other "transfinite numbers"—which are still more infinite. He created an arithmetic for handling such infinite sets—a weapon, as it were, with which mathematicians could cut their age-old bugaboo of infinity down to several logical sizes.

Although sets are more inclusive than groups, group theory has been called the supreme art of mathematical abstraction. Its principal pioneer was a tragic young 19th Century Frenchman, Evariste Galois. Poor Galois launched group theory for equations as a precocious teenager beset by the disapproval of his elders. He recorded the bulk of his life's work in an almost unintelligible, 31-page document scribbled during the last night of his life, when he was just 20. The next morning he died in a senseless duel over politics and a girl he hardly knew.

Group theory gets to the bottom of what happens when one kind of mathematical operation is performed on different elements, or when different operations are successively performed on a single element. By such analysis it lays bare basic structural patterns in mathematics. An innovator stumped by difficulties can sometimes use group theory to cross over into other branches of mathematics and borrow tools, methods or simply precedents which enable him to push ahead with his work. The theory also helps scientists when they glimpse patterns darkly in nature. It has been used, for instance, to analyze configurations of molecules and crystals—arrangements important in the chemistry of human genes or in the "solid circuits" of sophisticated electronics.

All manner of mathematical objects behave as groups. For instance, an equilateral triangle can sit on any of its three sides and still look the same. The rotations that carry the triangle from one of these posi-

A SYMBOLIC VIEW
THROUGH ALICE'S LOOKING GLASS

Lewis Carroll's famous Alice gets entangled in many a verbal jungle in the wonderland on the other side of the looking glass, but much of the tangled verbiage can be hacked away by the sharp blade of symbolic logic. Before this can be done, however, the sentences in question must be translated into the appropriate mathematical symbols. A simple example is where the White Knight tells Alice he has written a song, and ". . . either it brings the tears into their eyes or else—" "Or else what?" asks Alice. "Or else it doesn't. . . ." says the Knight.

Dr. Ernest Nagel, professor of philosophy at Columbia University, has translated this conversation into symbolic logic which involves the following special notation:
'($\exists x$)' means 'there exists x such that . . .'
'$\equiv$' means 'if and only if . . .'
'$\supset$' means 'if . . . then . . .'
'v' means 'or . . .'
'$\sim$' means 'not' and makes the statement following it negated.
Using this notation, and abbreviating the Knight's Song to KS, letting y stand for any song, z for any listener and t for any time, logicians could translate the Knight's rigamarole into:
($\exists x$) (y) (z) (t) ((y is a KS $\equiv$ x is a KS). (z hears the Knight sing x at time t $\supset$ ((x brings tears to the eyes of z at time t) v $\sim$ (x brings tears to the eyes of z at time t))).

While such a snarl of symbols may seem incomprehensible, it has a clear and precise meaning to the logician which plain words do not have. In jungles much thicker than Alice's, symbolic logic has been used successfully to blaze a trail to the heart of the meaning of vague or complex arguments in law and metaphysics.

tions to another constitute a group. What is more, this group has a structural counterpart in a certain group of permutations and in a group formed by the solutions to a particular cubic equation. All three groups are realizations of a single "abstract group." Thus the same abstract group covers cases from three separate realms: geometry, the arithmetic of arrangements and algebra. In abstract groups the most unlikely scions of mathematics turn out to be close kin—the same abstract logic masquerading under different disguises.

The deft changes which group theory works on one kind of mathematical creature to make it into some other kind of creature are known as "transformations." An algebraic equation is transformed when, for example, every x in it is replaced by a $y - 5$. A geometric figure in a plane is transformed when it is stretched or when its shadow is projected onto a different surface or into a different kind of space. It was a group of algebraic transformations, devised by a Dutch physicist, Hendrik A. Lorentz, to deal with certain problems in electricity, which Einstein seized hold of in constructing Special Relativity.

During transformations some aspect of an equation or of a geometric shape may remain stubbornly unchanged. Such solid islands are called "invariants." They may be no more noticeable than the invariant twinkle in the eye of a stock-company actor who plays Hamlet and Professor Higgins on alternate nights, but mathematicians seek them out and cling to them because they provide the most significant clues of all to underlying identities. An idea of the importance attached to them can be gleaned from a group-theory definition of geometry as "the study of the invariants of geometric configurations under groups of transformations."

The most introspective of the supermaths which help 20th Century analysts find their way is symbolic logic: a notation for stating and manipulating all sorts of propositions so as to bring both sequiturs and non sequiturs into mercilessly sharp relief. Through symbolic logic—whose flavor can be sampled in the extract from Lewis Carroll on page 173 —mathematicians have undertaken a Sisyphean task: to classify and analyze the thoughts involved in every branch of mathematics, with the aim of identifying the axioms and procedures at the base of each and of reducing all possible proofs to the barest skeletons. By this plan the results should be absolutely abstract and clear-cut statements like "if axiom A is granted then theorem B follows," which in one symbolic logical script would be written as $A \supset B$, or "if either A or B is granted then the negative of C follows," which would be set down as $A \lor B \supset \sim C$. Several monumental efforts have been made to translate all mathematical reasoning into such revealing shorthand—most notably in the three symbol-heavy tomes of the *Principia Mathematica*, published by Alfred North Whitehead and Bertrand Russell between 1910 and 1913.

A TEACHER OF GREATS
David Hilbert, from his post as professor of mathematics at Göttingen, Germany, influenced the entire world of modern mathematics. His work spanned the problems of two centuries—ranging from 19th Century algebra to modern logic and mathematical physics. His students included such future greats as Enrico Fermi, Robert Oppenheimer and John Von Neumann *(opposite page)*. Hilbert believed that all mathematical ideas eventually fit together "harmoniously." And it was his credo that every problem in mathematics can be settled—"either in the form of an actual answer . . . or by the proof of the impossibility of its solution. . . ."

Symbolic logic has produced one of the most curious and influential theorems in all modern mathematics. This is Gödel's Proof, an extremely abstract line of reasoning which shows that no useful branch of mathematics can be constructed on a consistent set of axioms without raising questions unanswerable within the framework of the axioms themselves. It is as if some structural property of a right triangle were forever unverifiable by the Euclidean axioms which lead to the Pythagorean theorem. For arithmetic Gödel's Proof demonstrates that all the possible relationships between whole numbers cannot be deduced from any one set of basic assumptions. The possible relationships or "truths" about numbers are as unlimited as the parade of numbers itself. For mathematics as a whole, the implication is that the subject will never be complete —that there is limitless scope for fishing in the mathematical ocean.

Kurt Gödel—now a member of the Institute for Advanced Study at Princeton—worked out his remarkable theorem in 1931 when he was 25 years old. He demonstrated it by what is called an "existence proof"—an argument which shows that something exists without necessarily producing the something for inspection. Gödel's theorem is variously regarded with antipathy or exhilaration. Those most hurt are the "formalist" mathematicians who had hoped to establish each branch of mathematics once and for all on a single consistent set of axioms. Those most gladdened are the freewheeling spirits who cannot endure the thought that mathematics will ever be cut and dried. One of the greatest of these was the late John Von Neumann, who played a leading role in the development of the atomic bomb. Von Neumann once said, "Much of the best mathematical inspiration comes from experience and . . . it is hardly possible to believe in the existence of an absolute immutable concept of mathematical rigor dissociated from all human experience."

Approach to a shifty adversary

One of Von Neumann's own major contributions, the theory of games, is one of the most practical mathematical developments of our time. It propounds intricate laws of strategy: how to adopt the best variations in play to avoid being beaten by a shifty adversary; how to make the best of a bad situation or avoid the worst of a good situation when faced by a fully rational, fully analytic competitor of known means and resources.

Game theory has been put to a gamut of uses. It has helped to determine the most profitable length of time a record company should wait between the releases of two sure-fire hit recordings; it has been employed, in a "blue-sky," or "think," contract let not long ago by the Office of Naval Research, to analyze the mathematical structure of competitive "American-type" economies. In a game that offers no clear-cut way of winning, game theory can show how to find the strategy which will come closest

A GIANT OF OUR TIME
John Von Neumann, whose mathematical "game theory" is now used in business decision-making and cold-war strategy, was famed for solving in his head problems that made other mathematicians turn to pencil and paper or even a calculator. Colleagues sometimes wondered, half-seriously, if his "lightning quick" intellect did not suggest "a species superior to man." His unique mind did, at least, set him apart from most men: after an automobile crash at Princeton, New Jersey, for example, he emerged from his wrecked car to explain, "The trees on the right were passing me in orderly fashion at 60 miles per hour. Suddenly one of them stepped out in my path!"

to achieving a stalemate. As a result, the idea of minimized maximum losses—called "minimaxes" or "saddle points" by Von Neumann—has been taken up by both camps in the Cold War, and may help to account for the indefinite postponement of World War III.

Between the difficult abstract logic of the formalists and the equally difficult theories of the Von Neumanns in modern mathematics falls the shadow of the high-speed electronic computers. Day by day, mathematics is being translated from elegant formulas into prosaic instruction sheets which the computers digest by mechanical brute force. A computer can solve problems which would leave a Newton or a Gauss gaping, and solve them to any number of decimal places, by purely pragmatic schemes of approximation, of endless try-try-and-try-again arithmetic.

Meanwhile pure mathematicians are climbing ever higher into new skies of abstraction. What they are accomplishing none of us really knows, because the equivalents of Relativity and atomic energy which may grow out of the mathematics of today may not be realized for decades.

As for the future itself, it is well described by one of the French collaborators in the work of Bourbaki, André Weil: "The great mathematician of the future, as of the past, will flee the well-trodden path. It is by unexpected *rapprochements* which our imagination would not have known how to arrive at that he will solve, in giving them another twist, the great problems which we shall bequeath to him."

Topology:
The Mathematics
of Distortion

At the far reaches of modern mathematics, some of today's best minds are working in a strange world of fascinating, improbable shapes. This field is known as topology. It is a special kind of geometry concerned with the ways in which surfaces can be twisted, bent, pulled, stretched or otherwise deformed from one shape into another. Sometimes topologists deal with surfaces that no one could construct; sometimes they conceive of forms that seem impossible—e.g., a surface with only one side. Their special world of pure mathematics ranges from seeming child's play to difficult abstractions that leave even the experts puzzled. Topologists like to quote a parody of *Hiawatha*, about an Indian who made some mittens of furry skin: "He, to get the warm side inside / Put the inside skin side outside" and "to get the cold side outside / Put the warm side fur side inside." In his mitten-twisting, the Indian was in fact performing a topological maneuver.

TOPOLOGICAL LOOK-ALIKES
A topologist is sometimes defined by fellow mathematicians as a man who does not know the difference between a doughnut and a coffee cup. But while he cannot turn a real doughnut (*opposite*) into a coffee cup, he can prove that doughnut and coffee cup are topologically the same, which means that in theory at least one can be transformed into the other, as shown on page 178.

A Topsy-Turvy World of Topological Changes

Most of the objects on these two pages—like the sphere (below) that changes first into a cube and then into a shapeless mass, or like the impossibly elastic inner tube on the opposite page—are undergoing what topologists call transformations. These are changes in the shape of a surface which leave certain basic properties unaltered—and the surface as a whole unbroken. To a topologist, a figure thus transformed has not really changed at all.

When a child picks up a ball of modeling clay, squeezes it into the shape of a box, then flattens it into a disk, he is performing topological transformations similar to those illustrated on this and the following three pages. What he has done is to deform the clay ball without breaking or tearing it.

All of the topological transformations demonstrated below involve a property called the "genus" of a surface. Roughly speaking, genus is defined according to the number of holes the object has—or, as the topologists say, by the number of nonintersecting closed or completely circular cuts that can be made on the surface without cutting it into two pieces.

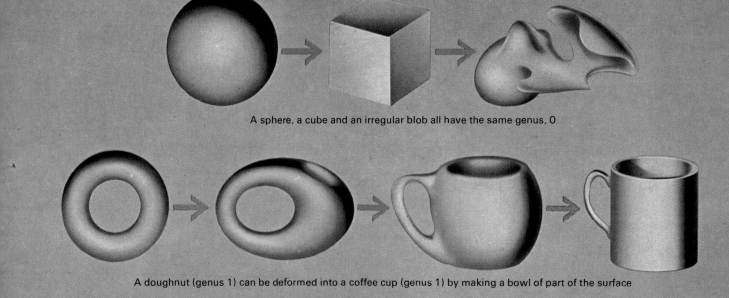

A sphere, a cube and an irregular blob all have the same genus, 0

A doughnut (genus 1) can be deformed into a coffee cup (genus 1) by making a bowl of part of the surface

A genus-2 surface, sugar bowl or vase, to a topologist is still a "lump with two holes in it"

MAKING TRANSFORMATIONS
In the three rows of topological changes above, the objects can be turned into each other—by twisting, bending or other shaping. But a sphere could not be turned into a doughnut, or a cream pitcher into a cube, without being broken—in other words, without making or removing a hole.

FINDING A GENUS
The three figures at right illustrate genus. No closed cut can be made around the sphere without cutting it into two pieces, so its genus is 0. Only one closed cut can be made in a doughnut without dividing it, so its genus is 1. Similarly, a two-holed figure has a genus of 2.

A sphere has genus 0

A doughnut: genus 1

Two holes give genus 2

TURNING A TUBE INSIDE OUT

In an exercise of topological imagination, an infinitely stretchable inner tube can be turned inside out without being torn. First *(upper left)* the valve hole *(outlined in red)* is stretched open. The opening is then successively widened until there is more hole than tube. Two twists *(steps 6 and 7)* turn the tube inside out; then the procedure is reversed. In the process the stripes inside the tube change direction.

TOPOLOGICAL TWISTING

Taking off a vest without taking off one's jacket is a simple, if strenuous, topological movement. The pictures below show one man's struggle to twist out of his vest. His success demonstrates that from a topological standpoint the vest was never inside the jacket at all.

THE GENUS OF EVERYDAY OBJECTS

Genus 0

Genus 1

Genus 2

Genus 3 or more

The wide range of familiar objects whose surfaces can be called topologically the same is illustrated on this page. In the row above, from left to right, are surfaces of genus 0, 1, 2 and 3 or more. Pictured below is the host of seemingly different shapes into which each of these surfaces can be topologically transformed. Surfaces with the same genus are in the same color.

THE TOPOLOGY OF A FACE
Distorted in a fun-house mirror, a man's face and its reflection are, topologically, the same: a point and its neighborhood on one correspond to a single point and its neighborhood on the other.

THE ONE-SIDED MOBIUS STRIP

A Möbius strip is easily made from an ordinary flat strip of paper: first the strip is given a half twist and then the two ends are connected to make a closed ring, as in the picture above.

"HALVING" A MOBIUS STRIP

When a cut is made around the middle of a Möbius strip, it might be expected to divide the strip in two. But when a line is drawn around the strip *(above)* and the strip is cut along the line, the result, as shown here, is not two strips but a two-sided strip. The mathematicians' explanation: a Möbius strip has but one edge; the cut adds a second edge—and a second side.

A Twisted World of One-sided Surfaces

Topologists enjoy creating odd shapes and strange objects. Among the most curious of these is the one-sided surface, introduced by the German mathematician and astronomer Augustus Ferdinand Möbius (1790-1868). In an article published after his death, Möbius described his remarkable paper surface as a strip which has no "other side." This one-sided strip, hard to imagine but easy to construct *(above, left)*, has all kinds of unexpected properties which are shown on these two pages.

Another German mathematician, Felix Klein (1849-1925), following Möbius' lead, devised a bottle with but one surface—i.e., it has an outside but no inside *(opposite)*. Such a bottle, if it could be cut in half lengthwise, would fall into two Möbius strips.

The work of Möbius and Klein has always fascinated laymen. Some years ago a limerick writer noted: "A mathematician confided/That a Möbius band is one-sided,/And you'll get quite a laugh / If you cut one in half, / For it stays in one piece when divided." Another poet finished the story thus: "A mathematician named Klein/Thought the Möbius band was divine./Said he 'If you glue/The edges of two,/You'll get a weird bottle like mine.'"

COLORING A MOBIUS STRIP

Anyone can paint an ordinary paper ring red on one side and green on the other. But, as one mathematician said, "Not even Picasso could do that to a Möbius band." If anyone tried, he would only prove *(right)* that the strip has only one side—on which both colors must meet.

A MOBIUS STRIP CUT IN THIRDS

A Möbius strip cut one third of the way in from its edge *(above)* produces a fresh surprise: the scissors make two complete trips around the strip but only a single continuous cut. The end result of this cut is two strips intertwined *(above, right)*. One of the strips is a two-sided hoop and the other is a new Möbius strip, with its one continuous side bounded by a single edge.

THE BOTTLE WITH NO INSIDE

This model of a Klein bottle, which has "no inside," belongs to topologist Albert W. Tucker of Princeton University. Nobody will ever see an actual Klein bottle because it exists only in the topologist's imagination. A true Klein bottle passes through itself without the existence of a hole, which is of course a physical impossibility.

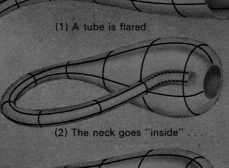

(1) A tube is flared

(2) The neck goes "inside" . . .

(3) . . . and is joined to the base

CONSTRUCTING A KLEIN BOTTLE

The three diagrams at left illustrate how a stretchable glass tube can be transformed into a Klein bottle: (1) one end of the tube becomes the neck, the other end becomes the base; (2) the neck goes through the side of the bottle; (3) the neck and base join, making the inside of the neck continuous with the outside of the base.

THE TWO-COLOR MAP THEOREM

One of the simplest map-coloring rules of topology states that if a flat map could be drawn entirely of straight lines which begin and end at an edge, it could be colored with two colors without having any adjacent areas of the same color. This is true no matter how many lines the map has. The three diagrams above demonstrate the theory. At left is a flat map in two colors; when a line is added at random *(center)*, two colors still suffice *(right)*. The colors below the added line remain the same, while all of the colors above it merely have to be reversed.

Map Coloring: The Topologists' Enigma

THE FOUR-COLOR MAP THEOREM

The simplest way to show that four colors are necessary for flat maps is to draw four regions so that each one touches the other three, as in the diagram above. Each of the three outside areas requires its own color, and the center must have still another. On the map that is shown below, three colors are sufficient for seven of the states illustrated, but the eighth state, Virginia, must be done in a fourth color.

Maps have always fascinated topologists because of certain qualities they possess, notably those involving color. It has long been the rule among map makers that whether a map is drawn on a flat surface or a sphere, four colors are enough to differentiate each country from all its immediate neighbors. The case for a flat map or a sphere is the same because any map on a sphere can be made into a similar flat map by puncturing the sphere and flattening it out. But there are cases where more than four colors are required. A map drawn on a Möbius strip requires six colors. And when a topologist rolls and bends a flat map into the shape of a doughnut (which he calls a torus), the map which once required only four colors may now need seven!

In all this, there is for the topologists one source of endless exasperation. They have been able to prove that only six colors are needed on a Möbius strip and seven on a torus, but no one has been able to prove what map makers have known for ages—that four colors are enough for any flat map or sphere. Topologists since Möbius' time have tried to draw a flat map on which five colors are needed: no one has done it, but neither has anyone proved that it cannot be done. It remains a great unsolved problem of topology.

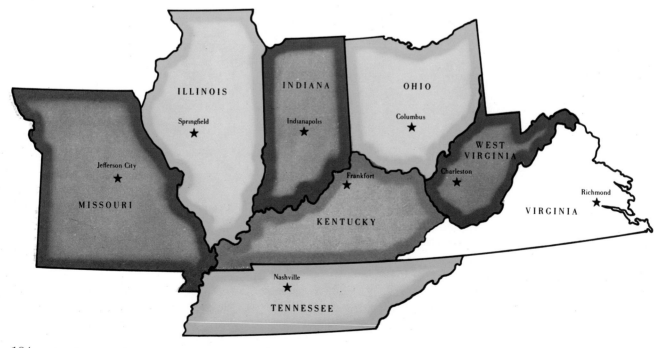

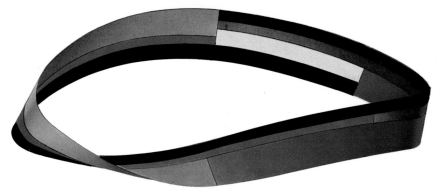

THE SIX-COLOR MAP THEOREM

On a Möbius strip, six colors are needed to ensure that no bordering areas on any map will be colored the same. Although a flat map can be drawn on an ordinary paper band using only four colors, if the band is twisted into a Möbius strip the same map may require six colors.

(1) Seven-colored map on a plane

(2) The plane is rolled into a tube

THE SEVEN-COLOR MAP THEOREM

Seven colors may be needed in any map on a torus or doughnut (right) so that no bordering regions have the same color. In the three figures here, two edges of a flat map are joined to make a tube; the tube's open ends are then joined, making the flat map into a torus.

(3) The tube is bent into a torus

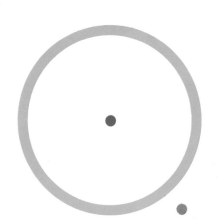

A SIMPLE CLOSED CURVE
A circle divides any flat surface on which it is drawn into two areas—inside and outside; any line drawn from a point inside the circle to an outside point *(above)* must cross the curve.

Noncircular Circles
and Mazes
with No Insides

To most people, each complex figure on these pages is a maze. But the topologist makes a distinction between the true mazes *(opposite)* and figures like the Jordan curve below. Topologically a Jordan curve is related not to the mazes at right but to the circle at left: it is merely a circle that has been twisted out of shape. Like a circle it still has an inside and outside; to get from one to the other, at least one line must be crossed. This can be seen by following the paths from either of the "dead ends" at the center of the Jordan curve; one lane leads out of the curve, the other lane ends inside.

Mazes are covered by another branch of topology, which is known as network theory. Because they have an entrance or exit, mazes can be said to have no inside; all of the paths in a maze connect to the outside without crossing any boundaries. Network theory provides a mathematical rule for getting out of any maze—but the rule itself is as complicated as a maze.

A JORDAN CURVE
A quick way to tell whether the two dots are inside or outside the Jordan curve above is by drawing a straight line from each dot to an area clearly outside. If the straight line crosses the curve an even number of times, the dot is outside; if an odd number of times, it is inside.

A LIVING MAZE
Garden mazes made of shrubbery were very popular in 18th Century Europe. The one above at Williamsburg, Virginia, is a copy of the most famous garden maze, at Hampton Court, England.

LOST IN AN ISLAND
This maze, designed by a British mathematician, has its goal in the center of an island of walls which, as shown by the broken red line, are disconnected from the other walls of the maze. Thus it is impossible to reach the goal by keeping one hand on the wall, as in the maze at left.

AN EASY WAY IN
In this diagram of the Hampton Court-type maze *(photograph above)*, the goal is the open area in the center. It is easily reached by the use of a simple rule: place either the left hand or the right on any wall and then take no paths which require that the hand be lifted from the wall.

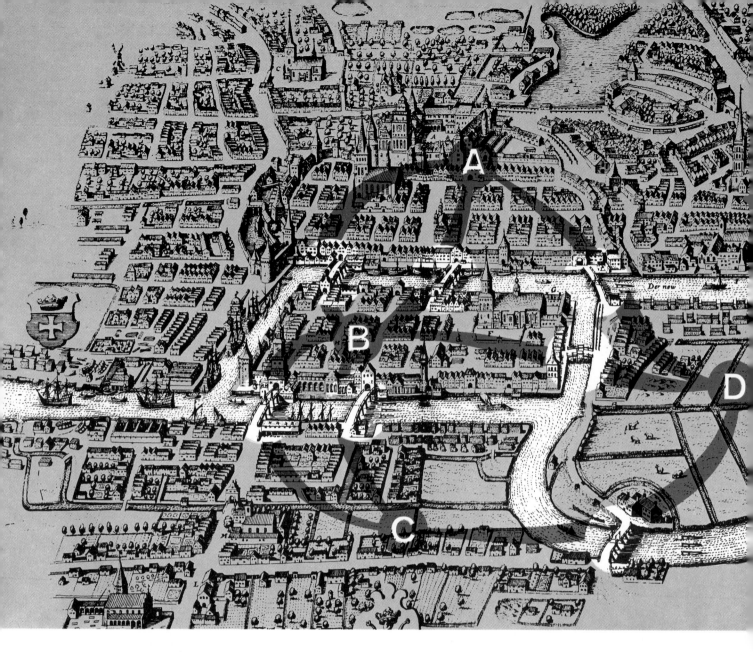

The Ancient Bridges That Led to Modern Network Theory

THE GRANDFATHER OF TOPOLOGY
Leonhard Euler (1707-1783) first studied for the clergy at the Swiss university in Basel. There the famed Johann Bernoulli noticed his skill in mathematics and encouraged him to change his career. Euler became one of the great mathematicians of all time—and one of the first investigators of the field later known as topology.

Network theory is one of the most practical forms of topology, with applications to electrical circuitry and economics. It was originated about 200 years ago by Leonhard Euler, who solved two problems in topology 100 years before topology had even been named. By sheer coincidence, both of these problems, which he thought unrelated, turned out to be part of what is now called network theory.

The two puzzles that interested Euler both concerned networks of lines connecting a number of points. The first involved the bridges of Königsberg. It had been a tradition among the townspeople that the seven bridges could not all be crossed in a continuous walk without recrossing the route at some point, but no one knew the explanation. When Euler heard of the Königsberg bridges, he realized an important principle was involved, and he proceeded to demonstrate mathematically *(above)* why such a walk was impossible.

The second of Euler's topological investigations concerned the many-sided objects known as polyhedra, which might be described as networks of points and lines in three dimensions. Studying these objects, Euler made a major discovery: no matter how many faces such a figure has, there is a predictable relationship among the number of its points, edges and sides. The result, which is still known as "Euler's formula," is explained at far right.

188

THE BRIDGES OF KONIGSBERG
The old map at left shows the Prussian city of Königsberg and the river loop that divides it into four areas (marked A, B, C and D). Connecting the areas are seven bridges (in the white circles). The heavy red lines indicate all the possible routes between A, B, C and D using the bridges. The diagram of Königsberg below—in which the lettered points and the lines correspond to those marked on the map—shows why it was impossible to cross all the bridges without recrossing at least one: in such a network, as Euler pointed out, some retracing is inevitable whenever there are three or more points at which an odd number of pathways converge.

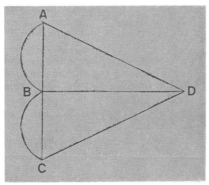

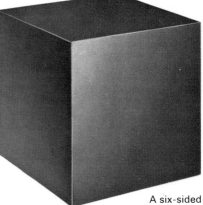

A six-sided polyhedron

EULER'S FORMULA
In any many-sided figure, or polyhedron, Euler showed, the number of edges plus two is always equal to the number of vertexes plus the number of sides. The formula is: $e + 2 = v + s$. Thus, a cube *(above)* has eight vertexes and six sides, and therefore 12 edges. The formula works as well for many more complex geometrical forms, like the 240-sided figure shown below. Known as a "solid starred small rhombicosidodecahedron," it always has 360 edges and 122 vertexes.

A 240-sided polyhedron

189

First a sheet is placed directly over its replica so that each point is located "over itself."

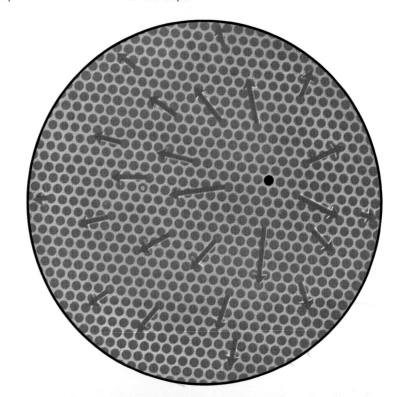

When the top sheet is crumpled, at least one point is still found over its counterpart.

The Odd Behavior of a Surface "Transformed into Itself"

Among all the transformations topology deals with, perhaps the most unusual are the ones shown on these pages. To the topologist, a crumpled sheet of paper and a disk with the various points on its surface radiating outward are both undergoing the same kind of change. They are, in the mathematician's words, "being transformed into themselves in a continuous fashion." That is, they are plane surfaces on which all possible points are shifting simultaneously in a flowing pattern, while keeping within the original boundaries. From such transformations, mathematicians have derived the "fixed-point theorem": when a surface is "transformed into itself" in this way, one point on the surface will remain where it was.

A TOPOLOGICAL REDHEAD
As the youngster at right shows, most human heads have a fixed point, in the form of a whorl, from which all the hair radiates. Topologically, it would be impossible to cover a sphere with hair—or with radiating lines—without at least one such fixed point. For the same reason the wind cannot blow everywhere over the earth's surface at once; there must be a point of calm.

A FIXED POINT ON A SHEET
Crumpling a sheet of paper *(above)* illustrates the "fixed-point theorem." First, a numbered paper sheet is placed over an exact duplicate so that all points on both of the sheets are aligned. Then the top sheet is crumpled above the bottom sheet. One point on the crumpled sheet must still be over its starting point. Here it is a point in the region of the number 78.

A FIXED POINT ON A DISK
Under the fixed-point theorem, if all the points around the black dot on the disk at right radiate outward in a regular flowing pattern—toward, but not beyond, the boundary of the disk—one point (the dot) must remain fixed. This holds true for any bounded unbroken area.

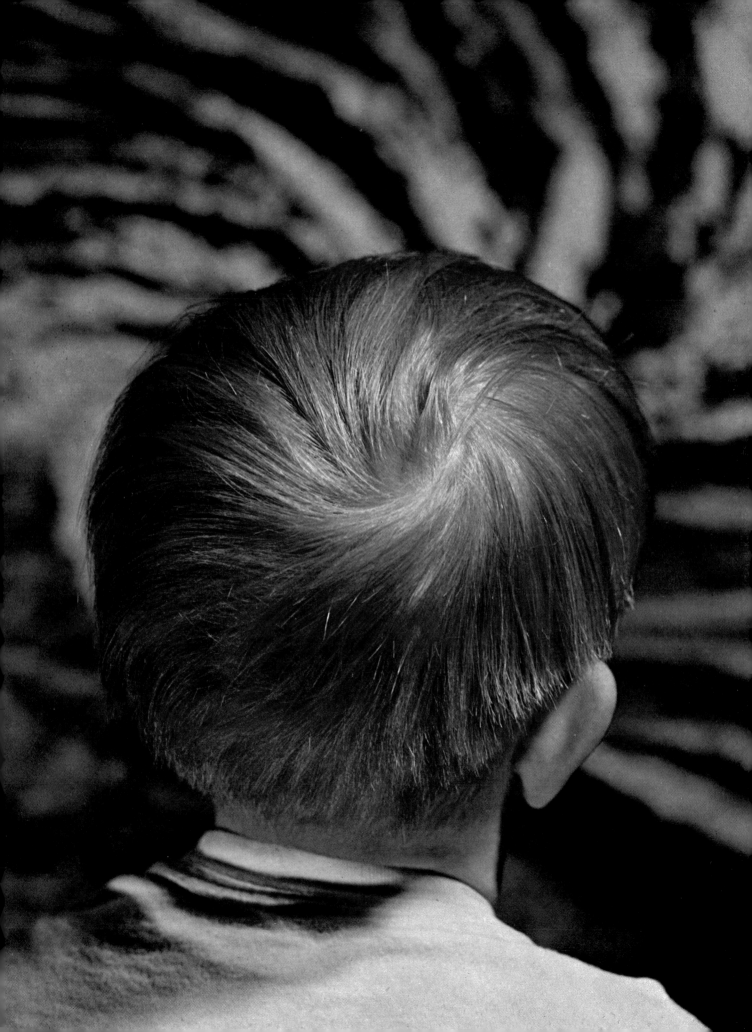

TRINKETS FOR TEACHING
An enthralled first-grader discovers the magical world of numbers with proportionately sized colored rods. Such aids are used in primary grades as a concrete introduction to many abstract mathematical relationships.

THE NEW LOOK IN HOMEWORK
A far cry from old-style arithmetic is this algebraic first-grade paper from an East Brunswick, New Jersey, school. By filling in boxes representing unknowns, children solve equations that include multiplying fractions.

The New Mathematics: Revolution in the Classroom

More and more, parents are finding themselves baffled by the strange mathematics homework their children bring home. Out of the mouths of babes who only yesterday uttered words of no more than one syllable they hear a vocabulary bristling with such formidable terms as "sets," "intersections" and "commutative and associative properties." This phenomenon reflects a change that has been sweeping through school mathematics for the past few years, setting traditional teaching on its ear and arousing sharp controversy in Parent-Teacher Associations and among mathematicians themselves. A goodly majority of the nation's schools are now trying experimental programs which may well set the tone for mathematics education of the future. Below, the LIFE Science Library answers some questions as to what this "new mathematics" revolution is about and where it may be going.

WHY THE CHANGE IN SCHOOL MATHEMATICS?

To SENSE a surge of creative excitement in a roomful of pupils is one of teaching's finest rewards. Until recently it has been only a rare treat for the teacher of mathematics. The 19th Century's demands for a steady supply of clerks, navigators and engineers made school mathematics little more than tedious drill in a musty subject whose fascination for some of history's best brains seemed inexplicable. Few youngsters came to college with the capacity or desire for higher mathematics. Science courses were delayed while students learned the elementary calculus to understand them.

Although drastic revisions in teaching had long been sought by mathematicians and educators, it took the national nervousness caused by Russia's Sputnik in 1957 to rouse public support and to loose the flood of federal and foundation dollars needed to speed the revolution on its way. Americans suddenly awoke to the fact that, like it or not, today's world rests on science, and that science in turn rests on mathematics. The urgent need is no longer for clerks and navigators but for men able to describe scientific findings accurately; for men able to predigest in equation form the problems

193

to be tackled by our ubiquitous computers and automation machines; and for men able to deal in the brand-new mathematics required to cope with Relativity (Chapter 8), quantum theory, and the systematic study of complex social interactions.

WHAT ARE THE NEW PROGRAMS LIKE?

Since 1952, more than a dozen experimental programs have been evolved by mathematicians, educators and textbook publishers. At last count these programs, with materials to suit, were being used to some degree in at least two thirds of the 135,000 elementary and high schools the country over. Most programs are being refined from year to year. The basic assumption is that no one can foresee specifically what kind of mathematics today's pupils will find most useful as adults. The innovators, in short, want to give them the understanding to make their own mathematics.

While differing in detail, all the programs seek a more precise mathematical language free of ambiguities and free, too, of misleading statements of the past. (How many of us were told, "You can't take three from two," and then a few years later learned that we could, getting −1 as the result?) From early on, youngsters are taught the essential "structure" of mathematics—the "why" rather than the "how"—through plane geometry (Chapter 2), elementary algebra (Chapter 3) and several innovations such as "number lines," "binary arithmetic" and "sets" (Chapter 8). Some have also been introduced to analytic geometry (Chapter 4), to probability (Chapter 6), vectors (Chapter 7) and Boolean algebra—all heretofore mostly in the domain of college students.

Fundamental to the new programs is the so-called "discovery" method of teaching, a far cry from the teaching-by-rote of the past. Through a kind of Socratic question-posing technique, students are gently steered into finding out for themselves about the world of numbers—into making and testing conjectures and devising rules for procedure, the premise being that what is intellectually intriguing is fun, and so learned faster and better.

HOW GOOD IS IT?

Almost no teacher who has taught one of the new programs wants to go back to the old. One teacher at New York's Hunter College Elementary School says that her second-graders protest loudly if she tries to skip a day's lesson in mathematics. Dr.

$$532 = 500 + 30 + 2$$
$$+ 219 = 200 + 10 + 9$$
$$700 + 40 + 11 = 751$$

BUILDING LARGE NUMBERS
"Expanded notation" reveals to primary-graders how large numbers are constructed of hundreds, 10s and units. Such aids clarify why numbers are "carried" in addition, a procedure that was formerly learned by rote.

Paul C. Rosenbloom, a University of Minnesota professor, recalls that he dreaded disciplinary problems when faced with teaching experimental mathematics to fifth-graders. He asked that experienced elementary teachers sit in. As it turned out, the monitors were indeed necessary—to shoo out the youngsters who clustered around Rosenbloom after class. University mathematics departments report an upsurge in majors largely as a result of the new programs—students coming in with far more un-

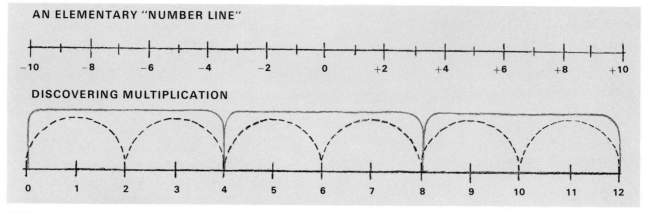

HOW NUMBERS ARE VISUALIZED
Through the "number line" a child discovers many mathematical relationships. On the top line, he marks off equal intervals to the right from zero to visualize the positive whole numbers. Marking to the left shows him the difficult concept of negative numbers. Soon he compiles his own multiplication table, using the lower line, by taking "jumps" of different lengths along the line, noting how many jumps of each length it takes to go a given distance. For example, it takes six jumps of two units each to cover the 12-unit number line, and three jumps of four units each.

derstanding of good mathematics than ever before.

Experts claim that we have underrated our children's ability to handle difficult and abstract mathematical material. "Actually," asserts Dr. David A. Page of the University of Illinois Arithmetic Project, "I can now teach third- or fourth-graders more about mathematical functions in one hour than I used to be able to teach college freshmen in two weeks. Furthermore, the young kids really understand, whereas many of the college kids didn't."

Page and others in the more experimental—and by no means universally endorsed—programs, such as Dr. Rosenbloom, who heads the Minnesota

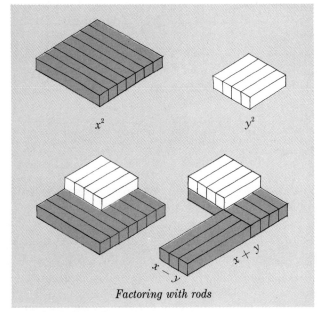

Factoring with rods

"SEEING" FACTORS
Square arrays of rods show what happens in the algebraic factoring of $x^2 - y^2$. If the block representing y^2 is put atop x^2 block, the area of x^2 left exposed can be rearranged to show its sides are $(x + y)$ and $(x - y)$.

School Mathematics Center, Dr. Robert B. Davis of the Syracuse-Webster Madison Project, and Dr. Patrick C. Suppes of Stanford University, foresee an educational breakthrough whose success in giving immature minds a mature grasp of mathematics will be incredible by present standards.

At the same time, the new programs are not without their caustic critics. PTA meetings resound with the complaints of parents convinced that their youngsters will not be equipped to handle simple arithmetical realities such as balancing checkbooks or figuring income taxes. Most such fears have been allayed somewhat by preliminary tests showing that pupils taught by the new techniques suffer no loss in basic skills. But many mathematicians and even some of the experimenters themselves feel that certain programs are too abstract and put too

THE UNIFYING IDEAS OF SETS

At the heart of many new school programs is a 70-year-old branch of mathematics called "set theory." Devised to give mathematicians a clearer look at the internal logic of their subject, it now permeates most of their advanced papers. By gaining an understanding of the way sets operate, children, too, can learn the elements common to arithmetic, algebra and geometry, thus gaining time in later schooling.

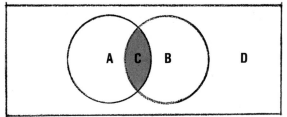

Instead of dealing with numbers alone, set theory deals with sets—well-defined collections of things. For example, all the zebras in the St. Louis Zoo make up a set, and the actual number of zebras is merely one property of that set. And instead of the addition, subtraction and multiplication that are performed on numbers, the operations performed on sets are called unions, intersections and complementations. These are partly illustrated by the so-called Venn diagram above, often used as an aid in visualizing sets. The union of set A with set B (read "A union B" and written A ∪ B) is represented by the total area bounded by the two circles. That is, it would be areas A + B − C, since otherwise the area C would be counted twice. The area where they overlap, labeled C, represents the intersection of the two sets and is read "A intersection B" and written A ∩ B. It refers to what is common to both sets. The complement of A ∪ B is another set, D, and is all the diagram outside of both A and B. Finally, the union of A, B and D, written D ∪ (A ∪ B), would be called E, a set represented by the entire rectangle.

To see how a sixth-grader might use set operations, take the following problem: "In a restaurant there were 15 people. Eight had hamburgers, six had malteds, five had both. How many had neither?"

Let E be the set of all people in the restaurant, D the set having neither hamburgers nor malteds, A the set having hamburgers and B the set having malteds. Then, n(E) is the *number* of people in the first set, n(D) the number in the second, and so on. The main equation for the problem is n(E) = n(D) + n(A ∪ B). As we have already seen, area A ∪ B is the same as areas A + B − C, so we can substitute n(A) + n(B) − n(C) for n(A ∪ B) getting n(E) = n(D) + n(A) + n(B) − n(C). Substituting the numbers, we get 15 = n(D) + 8 + 6 − 5. When we solve for n(D) algebraically, we see that six people had neither.

LEARNING THROUGH DISCOVERY

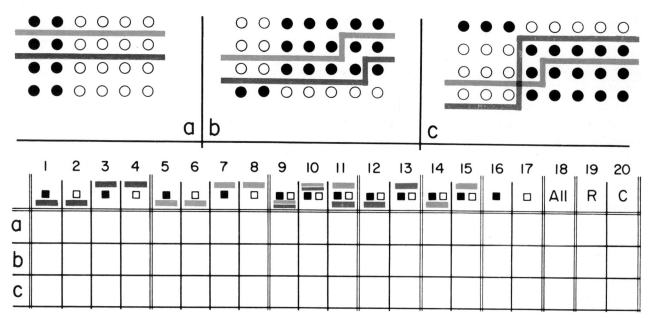

EXERCISE WITHOUT WORDS

A cryptic diagram such as the one above might be handed to a primary-school youngster in a new mathematics class with no other instruction than to fill in the blanks. Widely used in the "discovery" method of teaching, such exercises encourage children to look for patterns and relationships. In the process of doing so they get practice in counting and other arithmetic operations. The "secret" in the exercise shown here consists merely in deciding that a square over a line in the lower half of the diagram means to count the number of similarly colored circles occurring over the same colored line in the top half. Thus, in the first blank space on line A, the child would put a "2," in the second, a "4" and so on.

little emphasis on application to our everyday life.

The greatest stumbling block on the road to the new mathematics is the lack of teachers able to teach it. The more conservative curricula, such as the widely used School Mathematics Study Group program, were specifically designed to be taught with the least additional training for the teacher.

But to accomplish the revolution some experimenters hope for, present mathematics teachers will have to undergo massive re-education through summer and night courses, and will need a contingent of consultants to bail them out of daily trouble. Nevertheless, the revolution is under way. Mathematics education has broken free of its chains.

BIBLIOGRAPHY

General

*Bell, E. T., *Mathematics, Queen and Servant of Science.* McGraw-Hill, 1951.

*Boehm, George A. W., and the Editors of FORTUNE, *The New World of Math.* Dial Press, © Time Inc., 1958, 1959.

Courant, Richard, and Herbert Robbins, *What is Mathematics?* Oxford University Press, 1941.

Glenn, William H., and Donovan A. Johnson, *Exploring Mathematics on Your Own.* Doubleday, 1961.

Hogben, Lancelot, *Mathematics in the Making.* Doubleday, 1960.

*Kasner, Edward, and James Newman, *Mathematics and the Imagination.* Simon and Schuster, 1940.

Kline, Morris, *Mathematics in Western Culture.* Oxford University Press, 1953.

Land, Frank William, *The Language of Mathematics.* Doubleday, 1963.

Menninger, K. W., *Mathematics in Your World.* Viking Press, 1962.

*Newman, James R., *The World of Mathematics* (4 vols.). Simon and Schuster, 1956.

Smith, David Eugene, *The Poetry of Mathematics and Other Essays.* Scripta Mathematica, 1947.

History

Bell, E. T., *The Last Problem.* Simon and Schuster, 1961.

Cajori, Florian, *A History of Mathematics.* Macmillan, 1961.

*Smith, David Eugene, *History of Mathematics* (2 vols.). Dover, 1958.

*Struik, Dirk J., *A Concise History of Mathematics.* Dover, 1948.

Van der Waerden, B. L., *Science Awakening.* Oxford University Press, 1961.

Biography

*Andrade, E. N. da C., *Sir Isaac Newton.* Doubleday, 1958.

*Bell, E. T., *Men of Mathematics.* Simon and Schuster, 1961.

Cailliet, Émile, *Pascal, the Emergence of Genius.* Harper & Bros., 1961.

Dunnington, G. Waldo, *Carl Friedrich Gauss: Titan of Science.* Hafner, 1955.

Ore, Oystein, *Cardano, the Gambling Scholar.* Princeton University Press, 1953.

Special Fields

*Andrews, W. S., *Magic Squares and Cubes.* Dover, 1960.

*Boyer, Carl B., *The History of the Calculus.* Dover, 1959.

Boyer, Carl B., *History of Analytic Geometry.* Scripta Mathematica, 1956.

Cajori, Florian, *History of Mathematical Notations.* Open Court, 1951.

*Gnedenko, B. V., and A. Ya. Khinchin, *An Elementary Introduction to the Theory of Probability.* W. H. Freeman, 1961.

Keyser, Cassius Jackson, *Mathematics as a Culture Clue.* Scripta Mathematica, 1947.

McDonald, John, *Strategy in Poker, Business and War.* W. W. Norton. 1950.

*Newman, James R., *The World of Laws and the World of Chance.* Simon and Schuster, 1956.

Pfeiffer, John, *The Thinking Machine.* J. B. Lippincott, 1962.

Sawyer, W. W., *What Is Calculus About?* Random House, 1961.

†Weaver, Warren, *Lady Luck.* Doubleday, 1963.

Recreational Mathematics

Gamow, George, *Puzzle-Math.* Viking Press, 1961.

Gardner, Martin, *The Scientific American Book of Mathematical Puzzles and Diversions.* Simon and Schuster, 1959.

*Phillips, Hubert ("Caliban"), *My Best Puzzles in Mathematics.* Dover, 1961.

Steinhaus, H., *Mathematical Snapshots.* Oxford University Press, 1960.

*Also available in paperback edition.

†Only available in paperback edition.

ACKNOWLEDGMENTS

The editors of this book are particularly indebted to Carl B. Boyer, Professor of Mathematics at Brooklyn College, who served as general consultant, and to the following persons and institutions: Richard K. Bellman, RAND Corporation, Santa Monica, California; Harry Bober, Professor of Fine Arts, New York University; G. Waldo Dunnington, Professor of English and German, Northwestern State College, Natchitoches, Louisiana; Charles Eames; Howard F. Fehr, Chairman, Department of Mathematical Education, Teachers College, Columbia University; Henry G. Fischer, Assistant Curator, Department of Egyptian Art, Metropolitan Museum of Art; Roderick D. Graham, U.S. Weather Bureau; George Grossman, William Howard Taft School, New York City; Roderick C. Hodgins; Oswald Jacoby; Lemuel Jones, Instruction Manager, Education Department, Data Processing Division, IBM; Mark Kac, Professor, The Rockefeller Institute; John Kemeny, Chairman, Department of Mathematics, Dartmouth College; Kenneth Lohf, Assistant Librarian, Special Collections, Columbia University; Sidney Morgenbesser, Associate Professor of Philosophy, Columbia University; Raymond Pitt, Information Representative, IBM; Derek de Solla Price, Professor of Science, Yale University; Lewis Stark, Rare Book Division, New York Public Library; Victor Szebehely, Manager, Mechanics Section, General Electric Space Sciences Laboratory, Valley Forge, Pennsylvania; and Albert W. Tucker, Professor of Mathematics, Princeton University.

PRODUCTION STAFF FOR TIME INCORPORATED

Arthur R. Murphy Jr. (Vice President and Director of Production), Robert E. Foy, James P. Menton, Caroline Ferri and Robert E. Fraser
Text photocomposed under the direction of Albert J. Dunn and Arthur J. Dunn

XXX

Printed by R. R. Donnelley & Sons Company, Crawfordsville, Indiana,
and Livermore and Knight Co., a division of Printing Corporation of America, Providence, Rhode Island
Bound by R. R. Donnelley & Sons Company, Crawfordsville, Indiana
Paper by The Mead Corporation, Dayton, Ohio